INTRODUCTION TO HIGHER MATHEMATICS

CONSTANCE REID

A
P
O
L
L
O

E
D
I
T
I
O
N
S

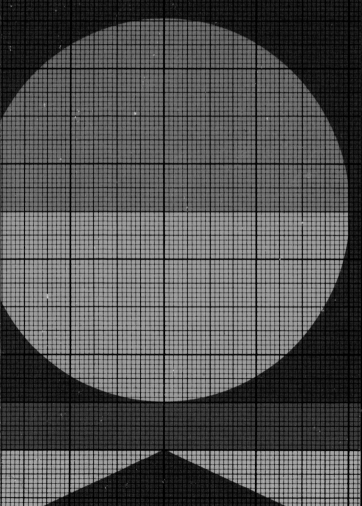

Introduction to

Higher Mathematics

for the General Reader

By the Author

From Zero to Infinity
What Makes Numbers Interesting

Introduction to
Higher Mathematics
for the General Reader

Constance Reid

Introduction to
Higher Mathematics

for the General Reader

Thomas Y. Crowell Company

New York · Established 1834

Contents

v

1

The Inexhaustible Storehouse

One of mankind's oldest, greatest, and most purely mental challenges is nothing more complicated than a sequence which is formed by making each member one unit larger than the one which precedes it.

0,1,2,3, . . .

When we try to unlock the secret of numbers, we grapple with the infinite. Never can we physically examine each number. Even if the task had been passed on, generation after generation, we would be no closer to the end than were the Greeks. The familiar numbers, so simple in their formation and yet so complex in their relationships, have cast a lifelong spell over some of the greatest mathematicians of all time. For anything which is learned about them must be learned by mental power alone.

"The higher arithmetic," wrote Carl Friedrich Gauss (1777-1855), known today and in his lifetime as the Prince of Mathematicians, "presents us with an inexhaustible storehouse of interesting truths—of truths, too, which are not isolated, but stand in the closest relation to one another and between which, with each successive advance of the science, we continually discover new and wholly unexpected points of contact."

These are the words of a man who lived under the spell of mathematics. Numbers were Gauss's first love. As a child of three, he is said to have corrected an error in the accounts of his father, who was a bricklayer; and throughout his life he so loved to compute that he devoted precious creative time to calculating the orbit of a newly discovered planet. His masterpiece, the *Disquisitiones Arithmeticae*, published when he was twenty-one, is devoted to pure number theory; and although he lived to be almost eighty and made inestimable contributions to many fields of science and to every branch of mathematics, he apparently never found any reason to change his often-quoted opinion that mathematics is the queen of the sciences—and arithmetic, the queen of mathematics.

Arithmetic (in the sense in which Gauss used the word) has also cast a spell over many men who were not, by profession, mathematicians. The most famous of these is Pierre Fermat (1601-1665), who was a lawyer. One reason for the amateur's interest in arithmetic is that it is almost the only branch of mathematics in which problems can be stated so that they can be understood by someone who is not a mathematician. Another is that in dealing with a subject he knows (such as numbers), the amateur is actually able to experience the intellectual appeal of mathematics. We may not be able to appreciate the functions of a complex variable, but we can all understand why the Greeks were fascinated by the characteristics of an infinitude of indivisible numbers.

In this chapter we shall try at least to glimpse the inexhaustible storehouse (about which the great mathematician Gauss wrote so glowingly) by examining some of the mathematically interesting relationships which exist between two kinds of numbers—the primes and the squares.

Although the classification into *even* and *odd* is the most ancient, the most mathematically suggestive classification of the numbers is into those which can be divided by some number besides themselves and 1 (called *composite*) and those numbers which can be divided only by themselves and 1 (called *prime*). The relationship which exists between the divisible composite numbers and the indivisible primes is so truly a key to unlocking the secrets of numbers that the theorem which expresses it is universally acclaimed the Fundamental Theorem of Arithmetic. Before stating this theorem, let us recall that by definition every composite number is divisible by some number other than itself and 1. This number which divides it must be prime or composite, since the classification is inclusive. If it is composite, it must be divisible in turn by some number other than itself and 1, and so on. This process ends when we come to a number which is not divisible by any other: in short, a prime factor of the original composite number. It is, therefore, easily seen that every composite number can be produced by the multiplication of primes or, inversely, can be factored into primes. The Fundamental Theorem of Arithmetic states simply that this prime factorization for any composite number is *unique.**

4	6	8	9	10	12	14	15	16	18	...
2	2	2	3	2	2	2	3	2	2	
×	×	×	×	×	×	×	×	×	×	
2	3	2	3	5	2	7	5	2	3	
		×			×			×	×	
		2			3			2	3	
								×		
								2		

* The numbers 0 and 1 are considered neither prime nor composite.

In the numbers above, we have factored 18 into the primes $2 \times 3 \times 3$. It can be factored in other ways: 2×9, or 3×6; but it cannot be factored into *primes* in any other way. By the Fundamental Theorem we know that the same thing will be true of a number like 18,674,392—or of any other number. We can thus work with any number n, no matter where it comes in the sequence of numbers, as a unique individual, not only because we know it has a unique place in the sequence (between $n-1$ and $n+1$) but also because we know it is a unique combination of prime factors $p_1^{k_1} p_2^{k_2} \ldots p_r^{k_r}$.* Yet, although it is deeper than the surface relationship between prime and composite numbers and although it is very important, the relationship expressed by the Fundamental Theorem is not so deep, or so intricate, or so completely unexpected as many others that exist among the numbers.

Those numbers which, next to the primes, have received the most attention from mathematicians are the squares: the product of some other smaller number multiplied by itself. Between the primes and the squares there are many interesting "points of contact"; yet the primes and the squares are different in many ways.

On the opposite page we have printed a table of the first fifty numbers in each classification. Let us first examine only the last digits of these numbers. Among the squares we see immediately that not one of them ends in 2,3,7 or 8; in fact, the last digits follow a pattern 0,1,4,9,6,5,6,9,4,1 which repeats indefinitely. Since, when we multiply a number by itself, the last digit of the product depends only upon the last digit of the number being multiplied, any number ending in 3 will have a square ending in 9, and so on. Obviously there are infinitely many squares ending in

* The k's indicate how many times a particular p, or prime, is a factor.

4

THE FIRST FIFTY SQUARE NUMBERS

0	100	400	900	1600
1	121	441	961	1681
4	144	484	1024	1764
9	169	529	1089	1849
16	196	576	1156	1936
25	225	625	1225	2025
36	256	676	1296	2116
49	289	729	1369	2209
64	324	784	1444	2304
81	361	841	1521	2401

THE FIRST FIFTY PRIME NUMBERS

2	31	73	127	179
3	37	79	131	181
5	41	83	137	191
7	43	89	139	193
11	47	97	149	197
13	53	101	151	199
17	59	103	157	211
19	61	107	163	223
23	67	109	167	227
29	71	113	173	229

each of the digits 0,1,4,5,6,9 and none whatsoever ending in 2,3,7, or 8. But when we examine the last digits of the primes, we find that aside from 2 and 5 all primes end in 1,3,7, or 9. Since all even numbers are by definition divisible by 2 and all numbers ending in 5, divisible by 5, it is apparent that primes can end only in 1,3,7, or 9. But the primes, unlike the squares, are very unpredictable in their appearance among the numbers. We know by a proof first given by Euclid (c.300 B.C.)* that the number of primes is infinite. But are there—as with the squares—infinitely many primes ending in each of the possible digits?

The answer is given affirmatively by a very deep theorem proved over a hundred and fifty years ago by P. G. Lejeune Dirichlet (1805-1859), Gauss's young friend, whose work opened up much of the *Disquisitiones Arithmeticae* for other lesser mathematicians. Dirichlet showed that every arithmetic progression of numbers

$$a, a + d, a + 2d, a + 3d, a + 4d, a + 5d, \cdots$$

contains infinitely many primes when a and d have no common factor. If we take $a = 1,3,7$, or 9 (the only possible endings for primes) and $d = 10$, we know that in each of the four resulting progressions there are infinitely many primes: infinitely many primes ending in 1; infinitely many ending in 3; infinitely many ending in 7; and infinitely many ending in 9.

1, 11, 21, 31, 41, 51, 61, 71, 81, 91, 101, · · ·
3, 13, 23, 33, 43, 53, 63, 73, 83, 93, 103, · · ·
7, 17, 27, 37, 47, 57, 67, 77, 87, 97, 107, · · ·
9, 19, 29, 39, 49, 59, 69, 79, 89, 99, 109, · · ·

The actual proof of this theorem, incidentally, is very difficult. It depends upon showing that the infinite series

* Euclid's proof rests upon the fact that if we multiply any group of prime numbers, the immediate successor of the number we get as our answer $(n + 1)$ will be either another prime or a composite number which has, as one of its factors, a prime not in the group of primes we multiplied. This is because no number, except 1, which is not a prime, can divide both n and $n + 1$. Euclid showed, therefore, that it would be impossible to have a finite set of *all* the primes because by multiplying them together we could always produce a prime *not* in the set.

formed by the reciprocals of the primes in each of the four progressions, such as

$$\frac{1}{19} + \frac{1}{29} + \frac{1}{59} + \frac{1}{79} + \frac{1}{89} + \frac{1}{109} + \cdots$$

is unbounded. This means, in less technical language, that if we add together enough terms we can have a sum greater than any number chosen, no matter how large. Proof is not easy, for there is no method by which one can predict the next prime in a progression, or the next member of a series.

If we look again at our table of primes and squares, we can see that it is no problem to write down the next entry in the column of squares: we simply multiply 50 by 50 and put down 2500.* But, to make the next entry in the column of primes, the best we can do is to examine the next odd number, 231. By inspection we see that it is divisible by 3, so we move on to the next odd number, 233. We try to divide it, in turn, by 3,5,7,11, and 13 (all the primes which are less than its square root) and since none divides it we can conclude that it is prime, and write it down as our next entry. This is the *only* general method for finding out whether a given number is prime.†

The classifications of the numbers which we have mentioned so far—even, odd; prime, composite; square and non-square—are so obvious that even if we do not usually think of all of them by name we cannot remember when we were not aware of them. Yet, among these groups of numbers there exist, in the words of the great Gauss, "wholly unexpected" points of contact. On the surface we have a not-unexpected relationship between the prime

* We can also add together the first fifty odd numbers.
† The largest known prime at the date of writing is $2^{3217}-1$ which was found prime by Hans Riesel, using the computer BESK in Stockholm. All the prime numbers below 50,000,000 are known.

numbers and the odd. All the primes with one exception are odd, since every even number is by definition divisible by the only even prime, 2. When we separate the odd primes on the basis of their remainders when divided by 4, all are either of the form $4n + 1$ or $4n + 3$. Certainly we have no particular reason for expecting that these primes, falling into two mutually exclusive groups because of their relation to the first non-trivial square number, should present us with any significant and unvarying difference in their relation to the squares. Yet they do. This difference becomes apparent when we attempt to represent each of the first few primes as the sum of two squares. With 3, 7, 11, 19, 23, 31, and 43, we have no success at all; but we find that

$$5 = 1^2 + 2^2$$
$$13 = 2^2 + 3^2$$
$$17 = 1^2 + 4^2$$
$$29 = 2^2 + 5^2$$
$$37 = 1^2 + 6^2$$

and so on.

It is immediately suggested that every prime of the form $4n + 1$ can be represented as the sum of two squares, while not one prime of the form $4n + 3$ can be so represented. The theorem which expresses this relationship is even more specific, for it further states that the $4n + 1$ primes can be represented as the sum of two squares *in only one way*. This is the classic Two Square Theorem of Pierre Fermat. Although it involves no mathematical concepts which are not familiar to a bright child, it expresses a profound point of contact among the numbers, and one of the most "beautiful" relationships in all number theory.

Fermat, unlike Gauss, did not fall under the spell of numbers until he was a mature man, established in the practice of law; but after he was thirty he pursued mathematics as an avocation. His professional quality as an amateur mathematician is nowhere better attested than in J. L. Coolidge's *Great Amateurs of Mathematics,* where he is omitted because, as the author explains, "he was so really great."

Fermat wrote to a fellow mathematician that he had proved the Two Square Theorem by what he called "the method of infinite descent." He began with the assumption that there existed a prime of the form $4n + 1$ which could not be represented as the sum of two squares; proved that if there were such a prime, there would have to be a smaller prime of the same form which could not be so represented; and continued in this way until he got to 5, the smallest prime of the form $4n + 1$. Since 5 can be represented as the sum of two squares, the original assumption was false; the theorem, as stated, was true. The extreme difficulty of this proof can be grasped from the fact that although Fermat detailed it roughly to the extent we have here, it was not until almost a hundred years after his death that a mathematician was actually able to prove the Two Square Theorem.

In addition to the Two Square Theorem, we have a Three Square Theorem and a Four Square Theorem, both of which reveal interesting relationships between the square numbers and all the numbers. Both theorems deal with the same relationship, the representation of numbers as the sums of squares; but the Three Square Theorem penetrates much more deeply into the relationship than the Four Square Theorem.

Every number, according to the Four Square Theorem, *can be represented as the sum of four squares.*

There is no better example in number theory of the fact that it is easier to state a truth than to prove it. A little computation is enough to suggest that four squares are probably sufficient to represent any number. The fact was probably known in the early years of the Christian era. It was then restated as part of a more general theorem, and proved by Fermat. Although Fermat remarked in a letter to a friend that no proof had ever given him more pleasure, he neglected to reveal the details to anyone, and the proof died with him. Leonhard Euler (1707-1783), one of the greatest, and certainly the most prolific mathematician who ever lived, then tackled the part of Fermat's theorem pertaining to the squares. In fact, off and on, he devoted forty years of his long life to it—without success. Eventually though, with the help of much of the work which Euler had done, the Four Square Theorem was proved by Joseph Louis Lagrange (1736-1813). A few years later Euler brought forth a more simple and elegant proof than Lagrange's of the theorem which had caused him so much difficulty, and it is now the proof generally followed.

For such representation of all numbers as the sum of four squares, we rely extensively upon the use of the square of 0, particularly in the case of those numbers which are squares to begin with or those numbers, like the primes of the form $4n + 1$, which are the sum of two squares. It is obvious from these that four squares are not by any means necessary to represent every number as the sum of squares. The question which then occurs is whether or not we can determine, by any general rule, the particular group of numbers for which four squares are necessary. This is exactly the answer which the Three Square Theorem gave. There is, according to the theorem, a particular group of numbers, the first of which is 7, that cannot be represented by any fewer than four squares; for all other numbers, three squares are sufficient.

Every number, according to the Three Square Theorem, *can be represented as the sum of three squares except those numbers of the form* $4^a(8b + 7)$.[*]

Now the Four Square Theorem is by no means trivial. Although the representation of the smaller numbers as the sum of four squares is easy to perceive, there is no assurance that as the numbers get larger more squares will not be required. Yet, when compared to the Three Square Theorem, which pin-points the specific type of number (and not an obvious, straightforward type, either) requiring four squares for representation, the Four Square Theorem is distinctly inferior—"much less deep," in the opinion of mathematicians.

To discover such deep relationships among the numbers, we must not look at them with jaded eyes. Youth, freshness, and perhaps even mentally standing on one's head all help. We also need a gift for seeing such relationships. There is one existing between the squares and the odd primes which is even more mathematically exciting than the one Fermat expressed in the Two Square Theorem, fully as deep if not deeper than the relationship expressed in the Three Square Theorem. But it would not even be observed by anyone who did not have the gift. Although this particular relationship had been observed earlier, the young Gauss (he was eighteen at the time) discovered it wholly on his own and was delighted with it. To him it was always the Gem of Arithmetic. More formally, it is known as the Law of Quadratic Reciprocity (quadratic meaning simply "of or pertaining to the squares").

The Law of Quadratic Reciprocity deals exclusively with the same kinds of numbers as does the Two Square Theorem of Fermat—the squares and the primes classified

[*] It was proved by Gauss.

according to the remainders they leave when divided by 4. Let p and q be any pair of odd primes; there exists a beautiful and delicately balanced relationship between these two apparently unrelated problems:

1. To find an x such that $x^2 - p$ is divisible by q.
2. To find a y such that $y^2 - q$ is divisible by p.

According to the Law of Quadratic Reciprocity, both problems are solvable or both unsolvable unless both p and q leave a remainder of 3 when divided by 4, in which case one of the problems is solvable and the other is unsolvable.

"The mere discovery of such a law was a notable achievement," writes E. T. Bell in *Men of Mathematics*. "That it was first proved by a boy of nineteen will suggest to anyone who tries to prove it that Gauss was more than merely competent in mathematics."

It took Gauss a year to prove the Law of Quadratic Reciprocity. "It tormented me and absorbed my greatest efforts," he wrote later. His was the first proof of this beautiful law and he published it proudly in the *Disquisitiones Arithmeticae* under the title of Fundamental Theorem. But he was not at all satisfied with his proof: ". . . it proceeds with laborious arguments and is overloaded with extended operations." In the next seven years he proved the Law of Quadratic Reciprocity in four more ways, using completely different principles. The first three of these four proofs, all of which he conceded were logically satisfactory, he dismissed as "derived from sources much too remote." The fourth he published with the frank statement, "I do not hesitate to say that till now a *natural* proof has not been produced. I leave it to the authorities to judge whether [this] proof which I have recently been fortunate enough to discover deserves this description."

The "authorities" apparently decided that it did, for this fifth proof (known as "the third" because it was the third one he published) is the proof which is universally used today. But Gauss himself could not have been satisfied: three *more* times in his life he proved the Law of Quadratic Reciprocity, his *Gem* of Arithmetic.

Lest we feel at this point that Gauss himself may have singlehandedly exhausted the inexhaustible storehouse of interesting truths which he found the natural numbers to be, we might mention that he went on to tackle the problem of *biquadratic* reciprocity where x and y are taken to the fourth power. A by-product of his solution was the creation of the theory of algebraic numbers, which we shall touch on in Chapter 2. Perhaps it is too much to mention that the general case of x and y taken to the nth power still remains in the storehouse!

It is curious that we usually think of arithmetic as the exact science, the science of right answers, the cut and dried science. But that is because we are thinking of the arithmetic of the elementary school, not the "Queen of Mathematics." In elementary arithmetic we perform operations on the numbers, first with accuracy, and then with speed. The ideal is most nearly achieved by the great electronic computers which, in spite of the awe they generate, can do no more difficult arithmetic than a high school boy or girl who is well trained; they can, however, do it faster and more accurately. An electronic computer is a mere drudge of the queen of mathematics. Although even Gauss loved to compute, he never confused his gift for calculating with his mathematical genius—or failed to perceive the queen's real challenge.

"The questions of the higher arithmetic," he wrote, "often present a remarkable characteristic which seldom appears in more general analysis and increases the beauty of the former subject. While analytic investigations lead to the discovery of new truths only after the fundamental principles of the subject (which to a certain degree open the way to these truths) have been completely mastered; on the contrary in arithmetic the most elegant theorems frequently arise experimentally as the result of a more or less unexpected stroke of good fortune,* while their proofs lie so deeply imbedded in the darkness that they elude all attempts and defeat the sharpest inquiries. Further, the connection between arithmetical truths which at first glance seem of widely different nature, is so close that one not infrequently has the good fortune to find a proof (in an entirely unexpected way and by means of quite another inquiry) of a truth which one greatly desired and sought, in vain, in spite of much effort. These truths are frequently of such a nature that they may be arrived at by many distinct paths and that the first paths to be discovered are not always the shortest. It is therefore a great pleasure, after one has fruitlessly pondered over a truth and has later been able to prove it in a roundabout way, to find at last the simplest and most natural way to its proof." †

The beautiful web of relationship perceived—then the fittingly beautiful proof discovered.

The beautiful proof—it is a tenet of faith with all who serve the queen—is *there*.

The inexhaustible storehouse awaits!

* It is interesting to note that Gauss first observed the Law of Quadratic Reciprocity when he was computing the decimal representation of all reciprocals through $\frac{1}{1000}$ in an attempt to find a general rule for determining the period of a repeating decimal.

† The quotations from Gauss are translated from the Latin by D. H. Lehmer and appear in David Eugene Smith's *A Source Book in Mathematics*.

VARIOUS CLASSIFICATIONS OF THE NATURAL NUMBERS

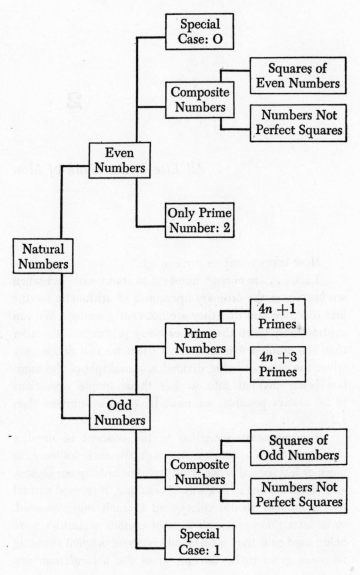

2

All Else Is the Work of Man

How many numbers are enough?

1,2,3, . . . are enough numbers to count with; yet when we encounter the ordinary operations of arithmetic for the first time, we find that they are not nearly enough. We can subtract only when the number being subtracted is smaller than the number it is subtracted from; we can divide only when the number being divided is a multiple of the number being divided into it. For these simple operations to be always possible, we must have more numbers than 1,2,3, ...

The necessary extension to the concept of number was a matter of centuries. Although we shall follow it in more or less logical order, it was neither orderly nor logical.

Numbers began as a way of counting. It seemed natural that a number should correspond to each thing counted, so in later times when all sorts of curious quantities were being used as if they were numbers, these original counting numbers came to be thought of as the *natural* numbers.

"God made the integers," thundered a mathematician of the nineteenth century.* "All else is the work of man."

Numbers other than the original natural numbers first turned up in the process of solving problems: computing, measuring, finding the roots to equations. Even mathematicians had curious attitudes toward them. Sometimes they ignored them completely. The Indian mathematicians did not consider the negative solutions to equations as solutions "because people do not approve of negative roots." The Greek mathematicians used rational quantities, or fractions, but refused to call them numbers; and the beautiful theory of numbers which they created deals to this day only with whole numbers. The mathematicians of the Renaissance, who solved otherwise unsolvable equations by acting as if -1 had a square root, uneasily dismissed $\sqrt{-1}$ (after they had used it) as "imaginary."

But in spite of the fact that they did not really believe that anything other than 1,2,3, . . . was a number, they ended up by justifying their use of these other quantities as numbers by the fact that they used them in the same way they used 1,2,3, . . . , adding, subtracting, multiplying and dividing them according to the *natural* Laws of Arithmetic. Addition and multiplication were always defined so that they were associative and commutative and so that multiplication was distributive with respect to addition. Then all man's work, they assured themselves, was at least logically justified by God's. That they were completely wrong about this does not reflect upon their achievement in extending the number concept to make the operations of arithmetic always possible. But we are getting too far ahead of our story.

To understand the extensions they made, we must be-

* Leopold Kronecker (1823-1891).

gin with a picture of the natural numbers marked off, unit by unit, upon a straight line extending indefinitely to our right.

$$
\begin{array}{ccccccccc}
1 & 2 & 3 & 4 & 5 & 6 & 7 & 8 \\
\end{array}
$$

Immediately we note a curious thing about this picture. While 1 marks the distance 1 unit from the beginning of the line; 2, the distance 2 units from the beginning; 3, 3 units; and so on, there is no number among the original natural numbers which can mark the beginning of the line. Yet if we take away, or substract, 4 units from the point marked 4, this beginning point is exactly where we obtain our answer. What *is* the answer to the question *How many is 4 minus 4?* The answer is none at all, or 0. So let us call 0 a number, since it answers the question *How many?* just as the other counting numbers do, and then let us mark the beginning of the number line with 0.*

$$
\begin{array}{ccccccccc}
0 & 1 & 2 & 3 & 4 & 5 & 6 & 7 & 8 \\
\end{array}
$$

Zero makes possible the subtraction of a number from itself.

But even with 0, subtraction is still not always possible. We still cannot subtract a larger number from a smaller and get as our answer a number that is on the line above. When we take 6 from 5, we find we are 1 unit short. In

---

* This is not at all the way that 0 was invented. It was invented, not as a number, but as a symbol to mark those columns in the representation of a number which contained no digits. The use of 0 made possible the representation of all numbers with only ten different symbols and was probably one of the most important practical inventions in the history of the world. The idea of 0 as a number (rather than merely a symbol) is not very important to anybody but a mathematician, to whom it is quite important. In the modern theory of numbers, 0 is usually treated as one of the *natural* numbers.

other words, we could perform the operation if we had one more unit to the left of 0. So, arbitrarily, we add it and an infinite number more of such units. We extend the number line indefinitely to the left of 0, and we mark it off in units just as we did the line on the right. Since these units are less than nothing we place a minus sign in front of them and call them *negative*. To be consistent, we must then place plus signs in front of what were once *all* the numbers, and call them *positive*. Zero, being nothing, has neither plus nor minus in front of it—is neither negative nor positive. The extended number line now looks like this, and we call the numbers marked on it the integers, or whole numbers.

$$-4 \quad -3 \quad -2 \quad -1 \quad 0 \quad +1 \quad +2 \quad +3 \quad +4$$

The negative numbers make subtraction always possible.

But now we come to division, and face to face with the unpleasant fact that most divisions do not come out even. If we are to perform the operation of division whenever it is indicated, we must have parts of numbers, divide our units into sub-units, and allow these as answers too. Unless we do so, we can divide a number only into a multiple of itself.

Although we shall indicate on our extended line only those sub-units obtained by dividing the unit in half and then in half again, we must understand that to make division always possible we have to include among our new numbers every quantity which can be represented by one whole number over another. We hardly dare think how many numbers we will have to add to the number line to make division always possible; for among the fractions every one of the integers (except 0) must be represented by an infinite sequence of itself over each of the original counting numbers in turn. We call these the rational numbers, since they express a ratio between two whole numbers. As a class, the rationals include the whole numbers, for these can always be expressed as the ratio of themselves over 1. With the extension of the number concept to include fractional parts of the unit, our line begins to look like this on the portion between -1 and $+1$.

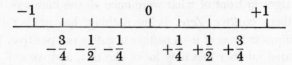

The rational numbers make division, except division by 0, always possible.

Things are getting a little crowded even with only the few numbers we are indicating on the number line. It is now, in fact, what mathematicians characterize as *dense*. This means that between any two rational numbers there is always another one. This is true no matter how close together we choose our two numbers. If m/n and p/q are any two rational numbers, the number formed by adding together their numerators and denominators, $m + p/n + q$, will fall between them. Between $\frac{2}{3}$ and $\frac{5}{7}$ we have $\frac{7}{10}$; and between $\frac{1}{356,821}$ and $\frac{1}{356,822}$ we have $\frac{2}{713,643}$. It would seem that we must have a number for every point on the line . . .

The Greeks, at the time of Pythagoras (c.500 B.C.), with only half as many numbers (for they had not extended their concept of number to include either 0 or the negative integers), thought that they had quite enough for all practical purposes, including the measurement of the universe, which they considered to be ruled by number. Every measurement of nature, they thought, could be expressed by 1,2,3, . . . and their ratios. Probably the most intellectually shattering discovery in the history of mathematics was the discovery that this beautiful array of numbers was not enough to furnish an exact measurement of the unit square.

We know (and Pythagoras, of course, and his followers knew) that the square of the hypotenuse of the right triangle is equal to the sum of the squares of the other two sides. When the sides of the triangle are 3 and 4, for example, the sum of their squares is 25, which is a perfect square, and the hypotenuse, or $\sqrt{25}$, is 5. But when we apply the same system to the unit square we get $1^2 + 1^2 = 2$ and the hypotenuse, therefore, is $\sqrt{2}$.

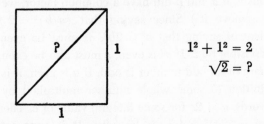

$$1^2 + 1^2 = 2$$
$$\sqrt{2} = ?$$

It is easy to see that $\sqrt{2}$ cannot be a whole number, since $1^2 = 1$ and $2^2 = 4$; but we can't help feeling that if we lay the diagonal out on that dense line of rationals, we shall find a number that exactly coincides with its length. Laying the diagonal out on the number line is merely a figurative expression, for our eyes could not detect the exact point on the line which marked its end, and there would be an infinitude of numbers which would appear to us to measure it *exactly*. In order to measure the diagonal of the unit square, we must use our minds, not our eyes, to find a rational number which when multiplied by itself yields 2.

There is no such number.

This, the Pythagoreans themselves proved with finality. Their proof is such a jewel that we repeat it here for the rare reader who is not already familiar with it. It can be reread and enjoyed by the others. One mathematician, citing it to a lay audience as an example of a beautiful mathematical theorem, commented that the person who cannot appreciate it is unlikely to appreciate anything else in mathematics.

The proof begins by assuming that there *is* a rational number a/b such that

$$\left(\frac{a}{b}\right)^2 = 2$$

and that the number a/b is reduced to its lowest terms. (Obviously, if a and b did have a common factor, we could always remove it.) Since saying that $(a/b)^2 = 2$ is the equivalent of saying that $a^2 = 2b^2$, a^2 must be even since $2b^2$ is divisible by 2. If a^2 is even, a must also be even, since the square of an odd number is odd. If a is even, it is equal by definition to some whole number multiplied by 2; in other words, $a = 2c$ for some integral value of c. Therefore, $2b^2 = a^2 = (2c)^2 = 4c^2$, or $b^2 = 2c^2$. It is apparent now, by the same reasoning, that a is even and that b is also even. The rational number a/b, contrary to our assumption, is not reduced to its lowest terms, for a and b have the common factor 2. We began by assuming that it was possible to represent $\sqrt{2}$ by a rational number a/b with no common factor for a and b. When our assumption is proved impossible, it follows that there is no rational number which represents $\sqrt{2}$. The number which we seek is irrational: it is a number not among the rational numbers.

There is a story that Pythagoras persuaded the discoverer of this unwelcome truth to drown himself or that, with a little help, he perished in a shipwreck. But one feels, like the mathematician who felt that his pleasure in a mathematical proof of his friend's death would outweigh his sorrow at losing him, that the exemplary elegance of the proof of the irrationality of $\sqrt{2}$ would more than make up for the discovery that the whole numbers and their ratios were not enough with which to measure the universe.

In spite of their proof that $\sqrt{2}$ was irrational, the Greeks pursued it through the rational fractions until they came at last to a very close approximation. While the number 2 is exactly expressed by the fraction $288/144$, the fraction $17/12$ multiplied by itself yields $289/144$ and differs from the true value of $\sqrt{2}$ by less than $1/7$ of 1 per cent.

How many such irrational numbers are there? Merely an infinite number—and this in spite of the fact that, as we have seen, the rational numbers are dense upon the line. By multiplying a rational fraction by itself, we can never get a whole number as the result; therefore, all numbers which are not perfect squares, or generally perfect powers, of some other whole number must have as their roots irrational numbers.

Although we cannot find a rational number to represent $\sqrt{2}$ and cannot even place it accurately between two rational numbers, we can nevertheless mark on the number line the theoretically exact point which it represents. (It is only theoretically exact since our measuring instruments do not enable us to mark any point exactly.) To do this, we construct a unit square from the point 0; then, placing one leg of a compass at 0 and using the length of the diagonal of the square as a radius, we mark off a circle which cuts the number line at $\sqrt{2}$, which we know (by the Pythagorean Theorem) to be the length of the diagonal and, therefore, of the radius.

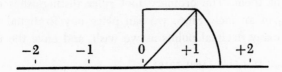

Here, in a sense, we have represented a cut which divides all the *rational* numbers into two classes A and B where every element in B is greater than every element in A. Such a cut is known as a Dedekind * cut and is one of several ways of stating what an irrational number *is*.

The irrational numbers make the extraction of roots of positive numbers always possible.

Up to this point we have been writing as if the successive extensions of the concept of number were things we would be unable to live without. Yet the great majority of people in even the most civilized countries do not consider 0 a number, but rather a symbol which is indispensable for the representation of numbers in the decimal system. It is most unusual to see the digits arranged in their natural order 0,1,2,3, . . . , 0 usually being placed, instead, *after* 9. Only of late, with the "count-down," has 0 been publicly recognized as a number, and then it is counted back to, rather than up from. Although we are all familiar with debts, losses, arrears and such unpleasant figures, we never put a minus sign in front of them in our accounts, but write them in red. We treat both profit and loss as positive quantities and subtract the smaller from the larger to find out whether we are ahead or behind, and by how much. We would find it difficult to live without the rational numbers since sub-units of the unit are necessary for even fairly approximate measurements; but considering the infinities of rational numbers—infinity upon infinity—which are at our disposal for measurement, we use practically none of them. The ordinary foot ruler distinguishes only to $\frac{1}{16}$ of an inch. Since we can place any irrational root to as many decimal points as we wish, and have the time

* Richard Dedekind (1831-1916).

and energy to compute, it is obviously of no great concern that we cannot place it exactly.

The truth of the matter is that the successive extensions of the number system took place, not to make the ordinary operations of arithmetic always possible in everyday life, but to make them always possible in algebra. This does not mean, even when we come to the final extension to the so-called imaginary numbers, that the successive extensions of the number system have no practical value. Algebra is one of the most practical subjects in the world. Just ask any scientist. But let us imagine for a moment that we are limited in our algebra to solutions for x which are positive whole numbers. Then let us try to solve the following simple equations by finding in each case a value for x.

$$x + 3 = 3$$
$$x + 4 = 0$$
$$3x = 1$$
$$x^2 = 2$$

Having extended the number system four different times already, we can now find roots for any of the equations above and for any similar but much more complicated equations. Yet, we are not through. There are still comparatively simple equations for which we can find no roots at all among the numbers we already have.

$$x^2 + 1 = 0$$

It is obvious that if we are to add 1 and get 0, x^2 must have the value of -1. Then x must have the value of $\sqrt{-1}$. But, under the rules by which the negative numbers were brought into the number system, it was implicitly stated that a negative number could not have a square root! Recall the rules for multiplying positive and negative numbers. A positive number multiplied by a positive number yields a positive number, as does a negative number multiplied by a negative number. $(+2) \times (+2) = +4$. $(-2) \times (-2) = +4$. Only when we multiply a positive and a negative together do we get a negative product. Since $+2$ and -2, for instance, are two different numbers and since by definition a square is the product of a number *multiplied by itself,* a negative number simply cannot be a square. But there is our equation, $x^2 + 1 = 0$! If we cannot come up with a square root for -1, we shall have failed in our avowed purpose of extending the number system so as to make the operations of arithmetic always possible. We shall have to concede that any equation for which x^2 is negative *has no root.*

Let us not give up too easily. In the first half of the sixteenth century Girolamo Cardan (1501-1576), saying frankly that roots of negative numbers were "impossible," nevertheless began to use them to solve otherwise unsolvable equations. Unfortunately he called them *imaginary* as opposed to *real* numbers when, as it turned out, they are no more imaginary than the real numbers, and just as real.

How can we go about finding such an "impossible" root for an equation like $x^2 + 1 = 0$? There is no root among the integers, the rationals or the irrationals. At this point we cannot change the rules under which we brought these quantities in as numbers. We cannot, for instance, say that a negative number multiplied by a negative number yields a negative number, for that would involve us in impossible contradictions. (It was to avoid the contradictions that we made the rule in the first place.) There is only one thing we can do: we can make up another number. We can simply *define* it as $\sqrt{-1}$ and call it i.

We have no everyday justification for what we are doing. We can compare the negative numbers to things like debts and temperatures below 0 and the years before the birth of Christ; but the number i we can compare to nothing in everyday life. It was for this reason that mathematicians, although they went right along using i to solve equations, felt a little guilty about what they were doing. God made the integers. If He had wanted man to have them, He would have made negative numbers and given them square roots!

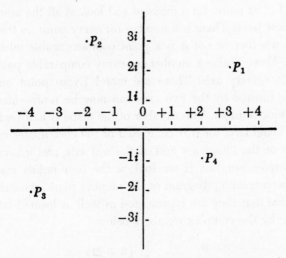

Today it is recognized that algebra is merely a formal symbolism with certain very useful applications. It cannot function and, therefore, will not be very useful unless the ordinary operations of arithmetic are always possible. Any extensions of the number system which are necessary means to this end are justified as long as they do not lead to contradictions in the algebra. It's as simple as that. So let us stop worrying about a justification for i and, after assuring ourselves that it is as logically consistent as anything else in the number system, including the integers themselves, let us get on with the business of solving equations.

Obviously i and its multiples ($2i$, $3i$, ...) cannot go on our number line, since they do not represent points on the line. They can, however, have a line of their own—the pure imaginary line which is perpendicular to the real number line at 0.

The imaginaries make the extraction of the roots of negative numbers always possible.

Let us pause for a moment and look at all the numbers we now have. There is a number for every point on the real axis, whether or not it is a point commensurable with our unit. There is also a number for every comparable point on the imaginary axis. There are more! Every point on the plane formed by the two axes can now be represented by a unique number. This number of the plane is half real and half imaginary, for it is composed of the coordinates of the point on the imaginary and on the real axis, and it is called a *complex number*. If we look at the four points marked on the preceding diagram of the number plane, we can determine that they are represented as well as located on the plane by the complex numbers below.

$$P_1 \qquad (3 + 2i)$$
$$P_2 \qquad (-2 + 3i)$$
$$P_3 \qquad (-4 - 2i)$$
$$P_4 \qquad (2 - i)$$

These complex numbers are represented abstractly as $(x + yi)$ where x and y are real numbers and i is defined as $\sqrt{-1}$. When x has a value of 0 the "complex" number becomes a pure imaginary $(0 + yi = yi)$, while when y has a value of 0 it becomes a real number $(x + 0i = x)$. The pure imaginaries and the reals are, therefore, merely sub-classes of the complex numbers, which are dense upon the plane.

Surely this last is an impressive extension of the number of numbers. But we are troubled. We saw that the extensions to 0 and the negative numbers made subtraction always possible; the rationals made division always possible; the irrationals, the extraction of roots of positive numbers always possible; the pure imaginaries and the number i that generates them make the extraction of roots of negative numbers always possible.* We now have a number for every point on the real axis and every point on the pure imaginary axis and, also, a number for every point on the plane. Surely these should be *enough* numbers to make the operations of arithmetic always possible and to provide every algebraic equation with a root! *But what about an equation like this one?*

$$x^2 - i = 0$$

Won't we need to extend our number system once again, beyond i to the square root of i?

The answer to this question is a very simple one, which mathematics can offer with all the finality of mathematical proof. The answer is no. We have gone as far as we need to go. It can be shown—and this is the Fundamental Theorem of Algebra—that any algebraic equation has a root within the system of complex numbers. To mathematicians i, the square root of -1, is the wonderful square root. In the satisfying language of mathematics it is both necessary and sufficient.

That pesky equation? Don't we need a square root of i to get a root for that? Oh no, $x = \pm \left(\dfrac{1 + i}{\sqrt{2}} \right)$. Multiply it out.

* $\sqrt{-2} = i\sqrt{2}$, and so on.

We have at last *enough* numbers!

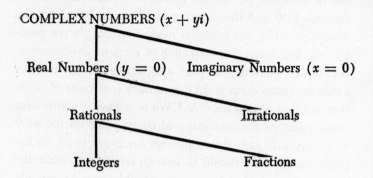

COMPLEX NUMBERS $(x + yi)$

Real Numbers $(y = 0)$ Imaginary Numbers $(x = 0)$

Rationals   Irrationals

Integers   Fractions

Multiplication Is a Vexation *

Although very few of us could state the Laws of Arithmetic on a quiz program, we obey them almost as unthinkingly as we obey the Law of Gravity. The Associative Laws, the Commutative Laws and the Distributive Law, as they are called, are no more than the formal statements of how the counting numbers behave under the operations of addition and multiplication and, by implication, substraction and division.

The Associative Law of Addition, for instance, tells us that when adding 1 and 2 and 3, we can perform the operation in several different ways and still get the same answer; and the Associative Law of Multiplication tells us the same thing in regard to multiplying.

* *Multiplication is a vexation.*
  Division's twice as bad.
  The Rule of Three, it vexes me,
  And fractions drive me mad.
  —Children's Rhyme

$$1 + 2 + 3 = 6 \qquad\qquad 1 \times 2 \times 3 = 6$$
$$(1 + 2) + 3, \text{ or } 3 + 3 = 6 \qquad (1 \times 2) \times 3, \text{ or } 2 \times 3 = 6$$
$$1 + (2 + 3), \text{ or } 1 + 5 = 6 \qquad 1 \times (2 \times 3), \text{ or } 1 \times 6 = 6$$

It is important to note that the Associative Laws do not tell us that we can change the order of 1, 2 and 3 when we add or multiply them and still get the same sum or product. This is reserved for the Commutative Laws.

We shall approach the Commutative Laws through a more social situation. We are all familiar with the fact that if we take 2 of something (like a cookie) and then 3, we shall have as many cookies as the person who first took 3 and then 2. If we take 2 cookies 3 different times, we shall have as many cookies as the person who reached for the plate only twice but took his cookies 3 at a time. These simple facts of social life are formalized in the Laws of Arithmetic to the effect that addition and multiplication are commutative operations: that is, $2 + 3 = 3 + 2$ and $2 \times 3 = 3 \times 2$.

[The Distributive Law merely brings addition and multiplication together with the statement that $2 \times (2 + 3)$ is the same as $(2 \times 2) + (2 \times 3)$, and in this chapter we shall not be concerned with it.]

We have actually seen that addition and multiplication, when applied to the cookies on the plate, are commutative; but do we know that they are always commutative in respect to things other than cookies? We probably think that we do, but let us take baseball hits instead of cookies. If our team gets a three-bagger and a home run, the total number of bases will be the same, whether we add $3B + 4B$, or $4B + 3B$; but there will be a considerable difference in the score depending upon which hit was made first.

$$4B + 3B = 1 \text{ run}$$
$$3B + 4B = 2 \text{ runs}$$

If we buy an insurance policy after we have an automobile accident, the result of the combination of accident and policy is quite different from what it would have been if the combination had been made in the reverse order.

$$\text{Policy} + \text{Accident} = \$1000$$
$$\text{Accident} + \text{Policy} = \$0000$$

There are many other examples in everyday life where the order of combination changes the result. We offer them only to show that while it may be impossible for us to think of 2×3 as not being equal to 3×2, we can think of ab, under certain conditions, as not being equal to ba.

But does multiplication have to be commutative among whatever quantities we choose to call "numbers"? Up until a little more than a hundred years ago, it was thought that it did; that—in fact—it must be; that the Commutative Law of Multiplication, like the other Laws of Arithmetic, was a logical necessity of number. We have heard the great mathematician say that God made the integers and all else was the work of man. This was the attitude of mathematicians from the time of Pythagoras. To facilitate measurements and the solutions of equations, mathematicians might have to extend the concept of number to include quantities other than the integers, but they could at least see that, like the integers which God made, they followed the God-given Laws of Arithmetic. In all the extensions of the number concept, from labeling the point at the beginning of the positive number line 0 to inventing a square root for -1 called i, this principle was followed. It was called the Principle of Permanence of Form; and it meant that the fundamental Laws of Arithmetic, which we have already examined, remained in force with the new numbers as with the old. This made everybody feel much better about using things like 0, −1 and i as *numbers*.

To be sure, a few small exceptions had to be made but these applied to laws which are deduced from the first five fundamental laws and not to the five themselves. For instance, division by 0 had to be prohibited; and for 0 and the negative numbers certain modifications had to be made in the law of multiplication which states that if a is less than b, then ax is less than bx. With the complex numbers a similar exception for addition as well as multiplication had to be made, since the complex numbers, being the equivalent of all the points on the number plane, are not linearly ordered. But these few exceptions were less important than might actually have been expected. The mathematicians had been so clever in defining addition and multiplication for their new quantities *so that* the Laws of Arithmetic would continue to hold, they can scarcely be blamed if they thought that their definitions were the only ones logically possible, and that the Principle of Permanence of Form proved that they were! God had made the integers and also, by implication, had made multiplication commutative. The mathematicians could look with complete satisfaction at the commutative multiplications of the new quantities they had included among the numbers.

$$0 \times 2 = 2 \times 0$$
$$(-2) \times (-3) = (-3) \times (-2)$$

$$\frac{3}{2} \times \frac{2}{3} = \frac{2}{3} \times \frac{3}{2}$$

$$\sqrt{2} \times \sqrt{3} = \sqrt{3} \times \sqrt{2}$$
$$2i \times 3i = 3i \times 2i$$
$$(2 + 3i) \times (3 + 2i) = (3 + 2i) \times (2 + 3i)$$

Surely, they thought, all this proved something. They were wrong, however. It was very pretty, and, more important, it *worked* in the manipulation and solution of algebraic equations. But it didn't *prove* a thing about the quantities being multiplied—except that in each case multiplication had been defined in such a way that it would be commutative!

Take the case of the complex numbers. The product of two complex numbers represented by number couples (x,y) and (x',y') was arbitrarily defined as $(xx' - yy', xy' + yx')$ *so that* the product of (x,y) and (x',y') would be the same as the product of (x',y') and (x,y). It didn't prove a thing.

Nevertheless, up until a little over a hundred years ago, it was the natural feeling of all mathematicians that the natural numbers had established the natural (and therefore the only possible) pattern for all quantities which were to be treated as numbers. To be numbers, quantities had to follow the Laws of Arithmetic.

The man to whom it first occurred that the Laws of Arithmetic were not a logical necessity of number was walking across a bridge at the time (symbolically, it might seem). The date was October 16, 1843, and we know it because he carved it into the stone of the bridge. His name (which he did not carve there) was William Rowan Hamilton (1805-1865).

For fifteen years Hamilton had been working on a generalization of the idea of complex numbers, a hypercomplex number which he called a quaternion. This generalization and its name arose naturally out of the fact that the numbers of the form $(x + yi)$, where x and y are real numbers and i is the square root of -1, can be considered more simply as couples of real numbers (x,y). We can then go on to number triples, quadruples (which Hamilton called quaternions), and so on.

Complex numbers, or number couples of real numbers, as well as representing the points on the plane, can also represent (and uniquely) all possible lines of all possible lengths radiating out from 0, or the origin. Such lines, or *vectors* as they are called, differ from the real numbers of the line in that they have magnitude as well as an infinite number of possible directions. The earliest numbers represented only magnitudes. The number system was a giant ruler, and any number could be uniquely defined as that length between itself and the origin.

1 _____

2 _____

3 _____

With the extension of the ruler to the negative numbers to the left of the origin, a number had to be defined by its direction (either positive or negative) as well as by its magnitude. When with the complex numbers we move into the plane, definition in this manner becomes more complicated. We have a number couple which has a magnitude, depending upon its distance from the origin, and a direction, which is one out of an infinite number of possible directions.

These vectors are not mere "angel flights," as they have been called, with no useful application to the phenomena of the physical world. The notion of a vector with the vector symbol ↗ suggests a force, but it can also represent a velocity, an acceleration, and so on. As such a representation, it has been extremely useful in mechanics. It does not, however, take any unusual degree of mechanical ability to recognize that the usefulness of this notion, algebraically as well as geometrically, is severely limited if we have an algebra only for vectors in the two dimensions of the plane.

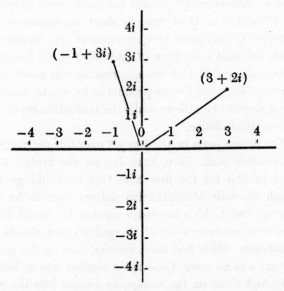

Hamilton was interested in working out an algebra for rotations of vectors in three-dimensional space, using a hypercomplex combination of four numbers—a quaternion. This meant that he must be able to perform all the operations of arithmetic upon his quaternions. It was his natural feeling (because it had been the natural feeling of all mathematicians who preceded him) that the operations of addition, multiplication, subtraction and division must always be performed according to the sacred Laws of Arithmetic: that the Principle of Permanence of Form, which had been maintained throughout all the successive extensions of the number system of common algebra, must be maintained at all costs, no matter how uncommon the algebra.

He had no difficulty in defining sum and product for two quaternions Q and Q' in such a way that the Associative Laws for Addition and Multiplication were upheld, and also the Commutative Law for Addition. Quaternion Q added to quaternion Q' yielded the same result as quaternion Q' added to Q—it was, in short, commutative. But quaternion Q multiplied by quaternion Q' was another and entirely different story from Q' multiplied by Q. Performed one way, the product of two quaternions was positive; the other way, negative! Define product as he would, Hamilton did not seem to be able to make the multiplication of quaternions commutative.

For fifteen years he tried to get over this seemingly insurmountable wall. Then, that day on the bridge, it occurred to him for the first time that he could go right through the wall. Multiplication did not *have* to be commutative, and in his quaternion algebra he would simply *define* it as non-commutative! He realized immediately that the difficulty which had been keeping him on the ground for years was no more. Quaternion algebra was at last airborne. And there on the bridge, he carved into the stone with his pen knife the date and the equations which defined multiplication among the quaternions.

It is difficult to describe what these equations meant for mathematics. They might be compared to the opening up of the West, the discovery of the Americas, or the setting up of colonies around Alpha Centauri. Yet none of these comparisons is quite the right one; for although it is true that they opened up a new world for algebra, a world in which the Laws of Arithmetic did not and did not have to hold, it is more important that they revealed the nature of mathematics itself—the homeland, as it were.

Perhaps quaternion algebra was something of a Declaration of Independence, for it freed algebra for all time from the tyranny of the natural numbers and their natural laws. Algebra, it announced, is a formal symbolism with useful applications. One of its most useful applications happens to be the manipulation of the real numbers; but it is not the only one. We can manufacture a symbolism, or an algebra, for anything we want—for the rotations of vectors in space, for example—and our only requirement is that it must not involve us in a self-contradiction. Then the symbolism which we have invented—no matter what we invented it *for*—can be applied to absolutely anything which can be defined so as to follow its rules. The x and y of algebra are not numbers, except as we choose to think of them as numbers, but are rather meaningless marks on paper which can be manipulated in any logically consistent manner we choose!

Although Hamilton's quaternion algebra was never as useful or as popular in physics as he had hoped it would be, it was followed by innumerable other algebras which do not obey one or more of the Laws of Arithmetic. All of them satisfy the Associative and Commutative Laws for Addition and the Distributive Law. It is in multiplication that they deviate from the traditional algebra of our school days. If they do not satisfy the Commutative Law for Multiplication they are known as non-commutative algebras; if they do not satisfy the Associative Law for Multiplication, they are non-associative algebras.

Among these new algebras, the most numerous are the non-commutative. Most popular is matrix algebra, which is in the direct line of descent from the quaternions of Hamilton, although it was invented by Arthur Cayley (1821-1895).

A matrix is a rectangular array of numbers, the size of the matrix being limited only by the length and number of the equations on which it is based. Some of the electronic computers work with matrices of more than a hundred members, but for our purposes the smallest matrices of four

39

members will be sufficient to illustrate the curious nature of multiplication in this algebra.

We shall first take two literal matrices, in one of which the small letters represent a set of integers; in the other, the capital forms of the same letters represent a different set of integers.

$$\begin{pmatrix} P & Q \\ R & S \end{pmatrix} \begin{pmatrix} p & q \\ r & s \end{pmatrix}$$

To combine, or multiply, these two matrices, we place the rows of the array on the left with the columns of the array on the right, multiply and add the products in each case. Thus row $P \quad Q$ from the left is placed on column $\begin{smallmatrix} p \\ r \end{smallmatrix}$ from the right to give us $Pp + Qr$; then row $P \quad Q$ is placed on column $\begin{smallmatrix} s \\ b \end{smallmatrix}$ for $Pq + Qs$. We follow the same method with row $R \quad S$, placing it in turn upon the columns of the right-hand matrix:

$$\begin{pmatrix} P & Q \\ R & S \end{pmatrix} \begin{pmatrix} p & q \\ r & s \end{pmatrix} = \begin{pmatrix} Pp + Qr & Pq + Qs \\ Rp + Sr & Rq + Ss \end{pmatrix}$$

The non-commutative nature of multiplication in matrix algebra is, however, most apparent when we multiply two matrices composed of integers rather than the literal symbols for them.

$$\begin{pmatrix} 1 & 2 \\ 3 & 4 \end{pmatrix} \begin{pmatrix} 1 & 1 \\ 0 & 1 \end{pmatrix} = \begin{pmatrix} 1 & 3 \\ 3 & 7 \end{pmatrix}$$

Then, when we change the order of the matrices being multiplied, we get a different product.

$$\begin{pmatrix} 1 & 1 \\ 0 & 1 \end{pmatrix} \begin{pmatrix} 1 & 2 \\ 3 & 4 \end{pmatrix} = \begin{pmatrix} 4 & 6 \\ 3 & 4 \end{pmatrix}$$

When we deal, as here, with matrices and their non-commutative multiplication of row upon column, we are certain that there can be no connection between such curious "numbers" and the numbers of the everyday world. Yet there is; for matrix algebra grew directly out of the way in which coefficients combine when one transformation of common everyday algebra is combined with another.

If we state the value of x in terms of y so that x has changed its form, we have a transformation.

$$x_1 = py_1 + qy_2$$
$$x_2 = ry_1 + sy_2$$

where p, q, r and s are all integer coefficients. If we then transform the value of y into terms of z, we have the transformation

$$y_1 = Pz_1 + Qz_2$$
$$y_2 = Rz_1 + Sz_2$$

where P, Q, R and S are integer coefficients.

Now if we substitute the transformation for y_1 where y_1 appears in our first transformation of x into terms of y, and so on, we find that our two sets of integer coefficients p, q, r and s and P, Q, R and S combine exactly as they would have if we had put them into matrix form and multiplied them together.

$$x_1 = (pP + qR)z_1 + (pQ + qS)z_2$$
$$x_2 = (rP + sR)z_1 + (rQ + sS)z_2$$

or

$$\begin{pmatrix} pP + qR & pQ + qS \\ rP + sR & rQ + sS \end{pmatrix}$$

If we now turn back to page 40, we see that here we have multiplied the same pair of matrices we multiplied there, but in reverse order, for a different product.

Surely though, we may say at this point, something like non-commutative algebra, which is undoubtedly a fascinating game for those with a taste for it, has no real practical value; for, as we all know, when we take two cookies three different times we always get the same number as if we had taken three cookies two different times—and that is the way things are. But we are wrong: it is not at all the way things are. The algebra which works very well for cookies will not work for quantum mechanics. It was in 1858 that Cayley invented matrix algebra. In 1925 it turned out to be exactly the algebra that was needed in the new work on quantum mechanics. Today, a century after Cayley invented it, so basic a tool is matrix algebra in a number of sciences that the writer of a recent textbook on the subject pointed out that in a modern course in matrix algebra the mathematics major is likely to find himself outnumbered, 10 to 1, by students whose majors are not in mathematics. Among those fields in which matrix algebra is extremely useful are aerodynamics, astronomy, electric circuit theory, mechanics, nuclear physics, quantum mechanics, as we have mentioned, and relativity!

Mathematicians wisely do not concern themselves with any usefulness other than mathematical usefulness. Today, freed at last from the Laws of Arithmetic, they invent new algebras at will.

The Laws of Arithmetic are for cookies!

4

Two Plus Two and All That

$2 + 2 = 4$.

This we know. All our lives we feel that it is something we can depend upon. It is our symbol for what is changeless in a changing world and, curiously enough, we are not so wrong. For the fact in which we have such confidence is a specific example of a most general property: a property which has provided mathematics and, through mathematics, the physical sciences with a scalpel for laying bare the very bones of structure. The changeless in a changing world.

How can something as simple as adding two numbers and getting a third of the same kind lead us to that which has been called "the most unifying concept of science"? To answer this question, we must begin by abstracting from the statement that $2 + 2 = 4$ the general property of which it is a specific example. Let us call our 2's a and b and say nothing more about them other than that they are members of the same class. (As a and b, they may be either the same or different members of the class.) Let us then call the addition represented by $+$ an operation, or a rule of combination, and designate it by *o*. Instead of $2 + 2 = 4$, we say that when *a* and *b* are members of a class, *aob* (the result of combining *a* and *b* by the operation *o*) is a member of the class. The property exhibited by *a* and *b* in respect to *o*, we call the *group property*. This is the first in a succession of abstractions which has made the branch of mathematics called "the theory of groups" something especially abstract even in a subject as abstract as pure mathematics.

To be sure that we thoroughly understand this first abstraction upon which all our others will rest, let us translate it back into the concrete. If 2 and 3 are members of the class of positive integers, and if we consider in order the common operations of addition, multiplication, subtraction and division, we find that the results $(2 + 3)$, or 5, and (2×3), or 6, are positive integers; but the results $(2 - 3)$, or -1, and $(2 \div 3)$, or $\frac{2}{3}$, are not. We say, then, that the positive integers exhibit the *group property* under the operations of addition and multiplication, but not under subtraction and division.

We have been using the words *class* and *operation* on the assumption that we know well enough what we mean by them; but before we continue we would do well to pause and define our terms in a more mathematically approved manner. We say that a *class* of objects is defined whenever a rule or condition is given whereby we can tell whether an object belongs or does not belong to the class. When we say "all positive integers," we have defined a class which does not include 0; but when we say "all non-negative integers," we have included 0 in the class which we have defined. Defining a class is not always simple. In some cases, as in defining what we mean by "mental" and "physical" phenomena in such a way that we could invariably place a given phenomenon, we can be stopped before we get started.

We say that an *operation* upon the elements a and b of a class C is defined if, corresponding to those elements, there exists a third thing c, called the result. In this general definition nothing is said about c being an element of the same class as a and b. When it is an element, and only then, the class has the group property under the operation.

$$a \, \varepsilon \, C \, \wedge \, b \, \varepsilon \, C \rightarrow aob \, \varepsilon \, C \text{ *}$$

This is the completely abstract statement of what is meant by the group property. Slightly less abstract, but enough so for our needs, is the following:

If a and b are in C, then aob is in C.

With this statement of the group property, we are now ready to proceed to the idea of *a group*. The word as used in modern mathematics means nothing so vague as the common "assemblage" of Webster. A mathematical group must satisfy four specific requirements. These are labeled in the way of mathematics, G_1, G_2, G_3 and G_4. We shall see immediately that G_1 is nothing more than the abstract statement of the group property which we have already met:

G_1 If A and B are in G, then AoB is in G.

We also recognize G_2 as the abstraction of the familiar fact that $1 + (2 + 3) = (1 + 2) + 3$ and $1 \times (2 \times 3) = (1 \times 2) \times 3$, what textbooks call the Associative Laws of Addition and Multiplication:

G_2 If A, B, C are elements of G, the results of operating upon the elements A and BoC, in the order named, is the same as the result of operating upon AoB and C, in the order named, or $Ao(BoC) = (AoB)oC$.

* ε = "belongs to," $\wedge$ = "and," $\rightarrow$ = "implies."

45

We shall find less familiar G_3 and G_4, but when we apply the test of the four G's to the positive integers we shall have no trouble recognizing the Identity and the Inverse, which are required by G_3 and G_4.

G_3 There exists in G an element I such that $AoI = A$ for every A.

G_4 There exists in G, corresponding to an element A, another A' such that $AoA' = I$ for every A.

Let us consider now whether the positive integers 1,2,3, ... , which exhibit the group property and observe the associative requirement with respect to addition and multiplication, meet the other two requirements for a group in respect to these operations. G_3 requires among the positive integers an I such that $A + I = A$. Since 0 is the only number which can be added to an integer without changing its value and since 0 is not included in the class of positive integers, we shall have to conclude that the positive integers do not constitute a group with respect to addition. In respect to multiplication, however, there is a number, the number 1, by which any integer can be multiplied without changing its value. $A \times 1 = A$. So the positive integers meet the first three requirements of a group with respect to multiplication. If they then meet the requirement of G_4, they constitute a group. But G_4 postulates the existence of a number which when multiplied by any member of the class will yield the Identity—in this case the number 1. There is no such number among the positive integers. To meet the requirement of G_4 we must enlarge our class to include the reciprocals of the positive integers: $\frac{1}{2}$, $\frac{1}{3}$, $\frac{1}{4}$, ... Then $A \times 1/A = 1$, the Identity, and we have met the fourth requirement for the Inverse.

If at this point, however, we conclude that the positive

integers and their reciprocals form a group with respect to multiplication, we will have fallen into error. Our *enlarged* class no longer exhibits the group property, although the original class did. When we add an integer and a reciprocal, or a reciprocal and a reciprocal, we get results which are neither integers nor reciprocals, and therefore not members of our class.

$$2 + \frac{1}{2} = 2\frac{1}{2} \qquad \frac{1}{2} + \frac{1}{3} = \frac{5}{6}$$

Doggedly, we enlarge our class once again to include *all* the rational numbers. And now, at last, we have *a group!*

But we have seen that the technical requirements for a group, although they are only four in number, can be slippery things. To discover whether or not we have them firmly in mind, particularly the requirements for the Identity and the Inverse, let us determine whether the classes and the respective operations listed below and on page 48 fulfill the four requirements for a group.

TEST

DIRECTIONS: Determine which, if any, of the four requirements for a group are met by each of the following classes. Which are groups?

	Class	Operation	G_1	G_2	G_3	G_4
1.	All integers	−	−	−	−	−
2.	All rationals	+	−	−	−	−
3.	All rationals	−	−	−	−	−
4.	All even numbers	+	−	−	−	−
5.	All even numbers	×	−	−	−	−
6.	All odd numbers	×	−	−	−	−
7.	1	×	−	−	−	−
8.	1, −1	+	−	−	−	−
9.	1, −1	×	−	−	−	−

10. 1, -1 $\div$ $-$ $-$ $-$ $-$
11. 1, 0, -1 $\times$ $-$ $-$ $-$ $-$
12. 1, i, -1, $-i$ $\times$ $-$ $-$ $-$ $-$

In the test and in our examples up to this point, we have been thinking exclusively of groups in which members of a class (like numbers) are combined by a certain operation (such as addition or multiplication). We can, however, think of a group as *a class* of *operations* which can be performed one after another (the rule of combination) to yield a result which could have been achieved by a single operation. For example, in the group of whole numbers (positive and negative integers and 0), the two operations "add -2" and add "$+5$" when performed in succession yield a result which could have been achieved by the single operation "add $+3$."

This concept of a group as a class of operations can be better understood when we examine a class of actual physical operations. Consider, for instance, the rotations in the plane which will turn a square into itself. The members of this class are four in number: the rotations of $0°$, $90°$, $180°$ and $270°$.

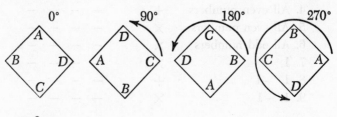

When we subject this class of four rotations to the requirements for a group, we find that they meet all four requirements, just as do the rational numbers, which we examined earlier.

G_1 — Any two rotations when performed in succession are the equivalent of performing just one rotation: the rotation of 90° followed by the rotation of 180° is the equivalent of performing the single rotation of 270°.

G_2 — The combination of rotations does not affect the result.

G_3 — There is an Identity, the rotation of 0°, which does not change the effect of any rotation with which it is combined.

G_4 — There is for each rotation another, an Inverse, which when combined with it returns the square to its starting point and is the equivalent of a rotation of 0°, the Identity.

By working out the various possible combinations of these four rotations we can construct a "multiplication table" for our group, where I,A,B,C are rotations through 0°, 90°, 180° and 270°, respectively.

$IA = A$	$AB = C$	$I_2 = I$	or		I	A	B	C
$IB = B$	$AC = I$	$A_2 = B$		I	I	A	B	C
$IC = C$	$BC = A$	$B_2 = I$		A	A	B	C	I
		$C^2 = B$		B	B	C	I	A
				C	C	I	A	B

This same multiplication table will work for other groups which do not, at first glance, appear to have any connection whatsoever with the four rotations in the plane which turn a square upon itself. If, for instance, we take the numbers 1, i, -1 and $-i$ and label them in order I,A,B,C we shall find that their multiplication is the same as that of the rotations.

$IA = A$, or $1 \times i = i$ $AB = C$, or $i \times -1 = -i$

$IB = B$, or $1 \times -1 = -1$ $AC = I$, or $i \times -i = 1$

$IC = C$, or $1 \times -i = -i$ $BC = A$, or $-1 \times -i = i$

$$I^2 = I, \text{ or } 1^2 = 1$$
$$A^2 = B, \text{ or } i^2 = -1$$
$$B^2 = I, \text{ or } (-1)^2 = 1$$
$$C^2 = B, \text{ or } (-i)^2 = -1$$

This should not surprise us when we recall our interpretation in Chapter 2 of the complex number plane as formed by two axes, of the real and imaginary numbers, placed perpendicular to one another. If we concentrate upon that portion of the real axis which is to the right of the origin (the positive reals), we can see that successive rotations of the number plane through $0°$, $90°$, $180°$ and $270°$ are the equivalent of multiplying the positive reals by 1, i, -1 and $-i$, respectively, in the figure on page 51.

The multiplication table for a group reveals to us what is called the *abstract group*. We have seen that the four rotations in the plane which turn a square into itself and the four roots of unity have the same multiplication table. We know, therefore, that they have the same abstract group, and we can now concentrate upon one group instead of two. What we learn about the abstract group we can apply as well to any group of four elements generated by the powers of one element. This means, among other things, that when in the investigation of some phenomena we come upon the hitherto-unsuspected pattern of our abstract group, the mathematics is already there and waiting for us.

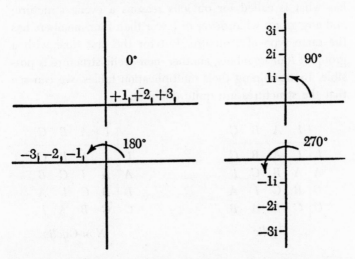

The recognition that several apparently disparate theories have the same abstract group may also result in the discovery of significant and previously undetected relationships among them. Consider the case of a group of rotations somewhat similar to our group of four. This is the group of all those rotations in space which turn a 20-sided regular solid, or icosahedron, upon itself so that after each rotation it occupies the same volume it did before the rotation. The abstract group of these rotations is also the abstract group of certain permutations which we come up against when we attempt to solve the general equation of the fifth degree. The same group occurs in the theory of elliptic functions. The relationship? It turns out that the general equation of the fifth degree, which cannot be solved algebraically, can be solved by means of elliptic functions. Such is the power of the group concept to uncover similarities among apparent dissimilarities.

But let us return for a moment to our small group of four elements generated by the powers of one element. It has what is called for obvious reasons a cyclic structure; and any group whatsoever of fewer than four members has the same type of structure. But for the first time with a group of four members, another, non-cyclic structure is possible. By examining their multiplication tables, we can see that the structures are quite different.

	I	A	B	C
I	I	A	B	C
A	A	B	C	I
B	B	C	I	A
C	C	I	A	B

Cyclic

	I	A	B	C
I	I	A	B	C
A	A	I	C	B
B	B	C	I	A
C	C	B	A	I

Non-Cyclic

When we try to think of a concrete example, or a realization as it is called, of the non-cylic abstract group, we are surprised at how many of our examples turn out to be cyclic. But let us consider a group of permutations or changes in the order of four elements, for which we shall use the numbers 1,2,3, and 4. The four operations I, A, B, and C are defined as follows:

I	Leave unchanged.	
A	Transpose 1 and 2.	(1 2)
B	Transpose 3 and 4.	(3 4)
C	Transpose 1 and 2, 3 and 4.	(1 2)(3 4)

When we perform just a few operations, we see the classic group pattern emerge.

	1	2	3	4
	1	2	3	4
Perform A	2	1	3	4
Then perform C	1	2	4	3

(We note that performing *AC*
together is the same as performing *B* by itself.)
Perform *B*   1 2 4 3

If these seem like somewhat childish occupations, we must remind ourselves that the theory of groups had its very beginnings in such manipulations of permutation groups; that permutation groups provided the long-sought answer to the question of when a general algebraic equation is solvable; and that permutation groups today are of great importance in the study of atomic structure.

The concept of the abstract group, which we have examined, is basic to the theory of groups; but in the application of theory to groups there are two other concepts of equal importance. Again, our cyclic group of the four rotations in the plane which turn the square into itself will serve for some easily grasped examples of these.

The first important concept is that of a transformation, which represents *change*. Three of our four rotations (the exception being the Identity) change in some way the figure to which they are applied. We have seen that when applied to a square, they turn it upon itself. When applied to an equilateral triangle, however, they have a somewhat different effect. The second important concept is that of invariance, which represents *changelessness*. Although the area occupied by the triangle does not remain invariant under the four rotations, many characteristics do: its shape, its size, as we see in the figure on page 54.

Rotations in the plane are relatively gentle transformations. Some are much more drastic; yet no matter how drastic they are, at least some characteristics of the figure subjected to transformation remain invariant. To illustrate this fact a little more vividly, we shall take a right triangle

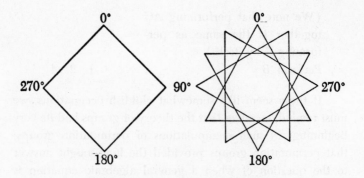

and subject it to several transformations. Under each type of transformation, some of the characteristics of the original triangle will remain. The list below is a partial one of these characteristics. The reader can select from this list those characteristics which remain invariant under each type of transformation shown on the following pages. Answers are on page 57.

SOME CHARACTERISTICS OF ORIGINAL TRIANGLE

1. Shape
2. Size and shape
3. Area
4. Size of angles
5. Length of sides
6. Number of sides
7. Number of vertices
8. Ratio of sides
9. Base
10. Height
11. Bounded by simple closed curve
12. Location on plane

INVARIANTS:

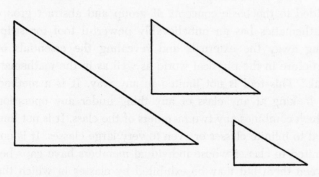

INVARIANTS:

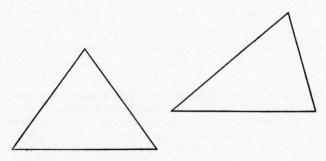

INVARIANTS:

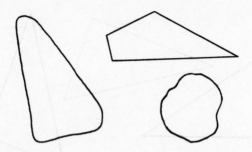

INVARIANTS:

With the concepts of invariance and transformation added to the basic concepts of group and abstract group, mathematics has an unbelievably powerful tool for stripping away the externals and revealing the essentials of structure in the physical world as well as in the mathematical.* This tool is not limited in any way. It is a method of looking at any class of any thing under any operation which combines any two members of the class. It is not limited to infinite classes or even to very large classes. It is not limited to classes whose individual members have gaps between them but may be exhibited by classes in which the individual members are, practically speaking, indistinguishable from one another. It is not limited to classes in which all of the elements are essentially the same or in which the same operation is performed upon every pair of elements. We have seen that the group concept is not limited to numbers. The idea of groups was first used in connection with

* Unfortunately, however, we can use it only where we have groups. In spite of the fact that there exist infinitely many groups, our chances that a particular class will meet the requirements for a group are relatively slim—just as our chances that a particular number will be a prime are slim, although the number of primes is infinite. For this reason we say that, in spite of the fact that the number of groups is infinite, *almost all* classes are not groups.

the solvability of algebraic equations: an equation is solvable if, and only if, its group is solvable. It was basic to a program which unified and defined the many branches of geometry: a "geometry" is a study of the invariants under a particular group of transformations. But the group concept is not limited even to mathematics. It exhibits itself in the structure of the atom and the structure of the universe.

Wherever we can apply the theory of groups, we are able to ignore the bewildering variety, to see among similarities differences and among differences, similarities.

The changeless in a changing world.

ANSWERS

A. Invariants: 1,2,3,4,5,6,7,8,9,10,11.
B. Invariants: 1,4,6,7,8,11.
C. Invariants: 3,6,7,9,10,11.
D. Invariants: 11.

5

Counting the Infinite

0,1,2,3, . . .

The three dots indicate to us that these numbers are enough for counting: that we shall never run out of numbers, for there is no last number. The counting numbers are infinite. They are also enough to count even the infinite, provided it is not too large!

Before we can understand this paradoxical statement, we shall have to revise our ideas about several things: about "counting," for one, and about "the infinite," for another.

It is quite possible to count without 0,1,2,3, . . . A bird that can tell when one of four eggs has been removed from her nest probably has a mental picture of the eggs in the nest with which she can "count" the eggs upon her return. Man's first numbers apparently consisted of such grouping pictures—man himself, bird wings, clover leaves, legs of a beast, fingers on his hand—with which other groups could be compared and "counted." If there were as many birds as fingers on his hand, and as many arrows as fingers, then he knew there were "as many" birds as arrows, and an arrow for every bird.

Formally we call what he was doing "counting by one-to-one correspondence" and we probably think of it as a rather inferior trick compared to counting with numbers. Yet what we are doing with our numbers is essentially the same thing. Say that we have a bowl of apples and a party of children. We count the apples and find that we have 7; then we count the children and find that we have 7. We have the same number of apples and children, so we have an apple for every child. We could also have handed an apple to each child and when we came out even we would have known, without knowing the number of children and apples, that we had "as many" apples as children. When we diagram what we have done, we see that in both cases we were counting by one-to-one correspondence very much like man with arrows and birds.

$$apple \longleftrightarrow child \qquad apple \longleftrightarrow 1 \longleftrightarrow child$$
$$apple \longleftrightarrow child \qquad apple \longleftrightarrow 2 \longleftrightarrow child$$
$$apple \longleftrightarrow child \qquad apple \longleftrightarrow 3 \longleftrightarrow child \ *$$

Counting by one-to-one correspondence is the most primitive and also, as we shall see, the most sophisticated method of counting.

The ancient method of directly comparing two collections to determine the number of members is the logical basis for a definition of what we mean by "number" which can be extended to infinite as well as finite collections. Let us firmly banish 0,1,2,3, . . . from our minds for a moment

---

* We have followed here the conventional method of beginning to count with 1; but 0 is logically one of the counting numbers and we can count just as well by beginning with 0. When we do, the answer to the question "How many?" is the successor of the last number which we paired with the last member of the collection.

and think instead of all the finite collections we might possibly want to "count" being grouped in such a way that all those which can be placed in one-to-one correspondence with each other—all the collections of a dozen members, for example—are in the same group. These groups do not need to be arranged in order of the size of their respective collections. For the moment it is sufficient for our purposes that they have been grouped. We have all those collections whose members can be placed in one-to-one correspondence with a dozen eggs, all those whose single member can be placed in one-to-one correspondence with the sun, and so on.

Model Collection	*Collections Which Can Be Placed in One-to-one Correspondence with Model Collection*
Day, Night	eyes, antlers, wings, man and woman, good and evil, . . .
Breakfast, Lunch, Dinner	ears and mouth, clover leaves, man-woman-child, stars in Orion's belt
Sun	head, self, earth, moon, god

Now, instead of having to keep in mind the specific collections we are using for our models, we can substitute an X for each member so that we have XX, XXX, and X. We can then easily arrange these new model collections in the order of their increasing size and, if we want, can give them names. We are now ready to define A, or whatever name we have given the model collection X, as the cardinal number of any class whose members can be placed in one-to-one correspondence with X, or the sun. If someone objects and says that all we have done is to define the number 1, why we shall be generous and call A "1." Then we shall call our next largest model collection "2" and define it as the cardinal number of any class whose members can be placed in one-to-one correspondence with XX, or Day and Night; and so on, to infinity.

The number of cardinal numbers we can define in this way is infinite, but the members of each class so defined will be finite. The number of members in each may be very large: all those classes whose members can be placed in one-to-one correspondence with all the stars in the Milky Way, all those whose members can be placed in one-to-one correspondence with all the grains of sand on the earth, all those whose members can be placed in one-to-one correspondence with all the electrons in the universe. It may be personally impossible for us to count all the members of a particular model collection, but they are "countable" in the sense in which we commonly use the word. The cardinal numbers which we have defined are finite cardinal numbers.

But is there any reason that in this same way we cannot define transfinite cardinal numbers for classes which contain an infinite number of members?

It is at this point that we must change our idea of "the infinite." For instance, instead of thinking of the counting numbers 0,1,2,3, . . . as an ever-growing pile filling room, world, universe, . . . , we must think of them stuffed, as it were, into the metaphorical suitcase of their class. In short, we must think of them not primarily as infinite in number but as an infinite class, something which we can handle as a unit, just as we handle finite classes, but something which is still different from a finite class because of the fact that it is infinite. This was not an easy idea, even for mathematicians, to accept. Yet once we accept it, we have something "capable not only of mathematical formulation, but of definition by number." These are the words of the man who, almost singlehanded, corralled the infinite for mathematics.

Georg Cantor (1845-1918) was one of those rare people who are able to look at the familiar as if they have never seen it before and thus become the first to see it. How revolutionary was his idea of the infinite, as *something consummated,* is shown by his own words in presenting it to his mathematical colleagues:

"This conception of the infinite is opposed to traditions which have grown dear to me, and it is much against my own will that I have been forced to accept this view. But many years of scientific speculation and trial point to these conclusions as *a logical necessity.*"

Once we have recognized counting as matching one class to another in one-to-one correspondence and an infinite number as something consummated—an infinite class—we are ready to take the next step, which is counting the infinite by placing one infinite class in one-to-one correspondence with another! Doing this, and even the specific way of doing it, was not original with Georg Cantor, living and creating in nineteenth century Germany and fighting an abstractly bloody battle not only with his colleagues but also with a mathematical tradition of the infinite which went back to the Greeks.

Three hundred years before Cantor, in the Italy of the Inquisition, Galileo had pointed out that the infinite class of squares can be placed in one-to-one correspondence with the infinite class of natural numbers: that there are fully "as many" squares as there are natural numbers, since every number when multiplied by itself produces a square.

Unfortunately Galileo, with Cantor's theory of the in-

62

finite in his palm three hundred years before Georg Cantor was even born, dismissed it:

"So far as I see, we can only infer that the number of squares is infinite and the number of their roots is infinite; neither is the number of squares less than the totality of all numbers, nor the latter greater than the former; and finally the attributes *equal, greater,* and *less* are not applicable to infinite, but only to finite quantities." *

What Georg Cantor did three hundred years after Galileo was to take the attributes of *equal, greater,* and *less* and apply them to infinite quantities.

When we take the first few numbers and set them off according to some of the various classifications which have been made, we come out with something like this:

All Numbers	Odd Numbers	Odd Primes	$4n + 1$ Primes	Square Numbers
0	1	3	5	0
1	3	5		1
2	5	7		4
3	7			9
4	9			
5				
6				
7				
8				
9				

If we total these various classifications, we find that among the first ten numbers we have five odd numbers, four squares, three odd primes, and only one prime of the form $4n + 1$. We have no trouble in determining that the class

* Galileo spoke here through the character of Salviatus in his *Mathematical Discourses and Demonstrations.*

of numbers from 0 through 9 is *greater* than any of its sub-classes, that the odd numbers and the even numbers are *equal*, and that the class of primes of the form $4n + 1$ is *less* than any of the other classes. If we attempt to place any of these sub-classes in one-to-one correspondence with the numbers from 0 through 9, we shall have at least five numbers left over. But what happens if, in following the same system, we take, instead of the first ten, *all* of the natural numbers and *all* of the members of the same sub-classes?

ALL Numbers	ALL Odd Numbers	ALL Odd Primes	ALL $4n + 1$ Primes	ALL Square Numbers
0	1	3	5	0
1	3	5	13	1
2	5	7	17	4
3	7	11	29	9
4	9	13	33	16
5	11	17	37	25
. . .	. . .	. . .	. . .	. . .

It is already apparent. The three dots at the end of each column indicate that each class of numbers is infinite; in spite of the fact that we appear to be exhausting some of the classes, like the $4n + 1$ primes, more quickly than the others, we only appear to be doing so. We can never exhaust an infinite class. When we consider a finite class of whatever size we please, the natural numbers in the chosen class will far outnumber any one of the sub-classes; but when we take all of them, they are *equal* to any one of the equal sub-classes.

Galileo said that they were neither more nor less, and that the attribute of *equal* was not applicable to infinite quantities. Cantor said that infinite quantities are equal when they can be placed in one-to-one correspondence with each other: they have the same cardinal number!

Just as we said that all classes which could be placed in one-to-one correspondence with the class of the sun, or X, had the same cardinal number, which we call 1, Cantor said that all classes which can be placed in one-to-one correspondence with the natural numbers have the same cardinal number, which he called aleph-zero or $\aleph_0$. It is different from the finite cardinals only in that it is *transfinite*.

We have already seen how sub-classes of the class of natural numbers can be placed in one-to-one correspondence with the whole of which they are a part; but so curious are the workings of infinite classes, as opposed to finite classes, that we can also do our pairing the other way around. We can set off in one-to-one correspondence with the natural numbers a class of numbers of which they themselves are a sub-class. The class of all integers has one peculiarity which its sub-class, the natural numbers, does not have: it has neither a last nor a first member. How, then, can we pair it off with the natural numbers? This is not as difficult as it might seem. It is merely a matter of ordering the integers in such a way that they can, as it were, stand up and be counted. With no beginning, we begin right in the middle at 0 and then count each pair of integers, positive and negative, in turn.

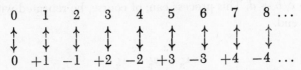

There is no particular trick to pairing the natural numbers with the integers, which include them as a sub-class; but such a pairing does serve to show an important technique in counting the infinite. A class of numbers which may not appear to be countable (in the case of the integers because there is no first number) can often be rearranged in such a way that it can be counted. Consider the class of all positive rational numbers. These are numbers of the form a/b where a and b are both integers. When a is smaller than b, we have what we called in grammar school a "proper" fraction; when b is smaller, an "improper" one. The class of all positive rational numbers is no straightforward sort of infinity like the class of integer squares where we have just one member of the class for each integer. Just one small sub-class, a/b where a is 1, is infinite in number. Since a may take any integer value and for every a, b may take any integer value, we appear to have among these numbers infinity upon infinity, an infinite number of infinities.

If we take the positive rationals in what might be called their natural order, omitting those with common factors since they are already represented, we find that placing them in one-to-one correspondence with the natural numbers is impossible. Not only is there no "smallest" fraction, but also there is no "next largest" fraction. Between any two a/b and c/d an infinity of fractions larger than a/b and smaller than c/d spring up to vex us. For between a/b and c/d we can always find an in-between fraction by adding the two numerators and the two denominators and getting $a + c/b + d$. This process can, of course, be repeated without end.

$$
\begin{array}{ccccccccc}
 & & & \tfrac{1}{3} & & \tfrac{1}{2} & & & \\
 & & \tfrac{1}{3} & & \tfrac{2}{5} & & \tfrac{1}{2} & & \\
 & \tfrac{1}{3} & & \tfrac{3}{8} & & \tfrac{2}{5} & & \tfrac{3}{7} & & \tfrac{1}{2} \\
\tfrac{1}{3} & \tfrac{4}{11} & \tfrac{3}{8} & \tfrac{5}{13} & \tfrac{2}{5} & \tfrac{5}{12} & \tfrac{3}{7} & \tfrac{4}{9} & \tfrac{1}{2}
\end{array}
$$

Obviously it is impossible for us to pair off with the natural numbers a class of numbers which behave in this fantastic fashion. We have sown dragon teeth on the number line.

But remember, we have said nothing about the rational numbers having to be paired off in their natural order—only that they must be paired in such a way that we can see that we are going to be able to count them with the natural numbers. So let us rearrange the rational numbers. Let us organize them into battalions: the first battalion consisting of all those rational numbers whose numerator is 1, the second battalion consisting of all those whose numerator is 2; and so on.

$$\tfrac{1}{1} \ \tfrac{1}{2} \ \tfrac{1}{3} \ \tfrac{1}{4} \ \tfrac{1}{5} \ \cdots \ \tfrac{2}{1} \ \tfrac{2}{3} \ \tfrac{2}{5} \ \tfrac{2}{7} \ \cdots \ \tfrac{3}{1} \ \tfrac{3}{2} \ \tfrac{3}{4} \ \cdots$$

This arrangement is reminiscent of one of those parades during which we wait restlessly for the band while an apparently endless procession of foot soldiers goes by. The only difference between our parade and the actual parade is that it is not just seemingly endless; it *is* endless. The band, or even the second battalion, can never pass by. Obviously, again it is impossible to count off by placing in one-to-one correspondence with the natural numbers a set of numbers which behaves in this fashion; for although in counting the primes, for instance, with the natural numbers we would never finish, we would always be able to count as far as any prime we might care to choose. With this arrangement of the rational numbers, not only could we never get to the end, but we could never get to $\tfrac{2}{3}$! Have we then come at last upon an infinity which is impossible to pair with the natural numbers, an infinity whose cardinal number is different from and perhaps larger than $\aleph_0$?

No, we have not.

The simple method by which Georg Cantor ordered the positive rational numbers so that they can be placed in one-to-one correspondence with the natural numbers has the quality of genius. All he did was to take the groupings which we have called battalions and arrange them in rows instead of in one long straight line.

$$\frac{1}{1} \quad \frac{1}{2} \quad \frac{1}{3} \quad \frac{1}{4} \quad \frac{1}{5} \quad \frac{1}{6} \cdots$$
$$\frac{2}{1} \quad \frac{2}{3} \quad \frac{2}{5} \quad \frac{2}{7} \quad \frac{2}{9} \quad \frac{2}{11} \cdots$$
$$\frac{3}{1} \quad \frac{3}{2} \quad \frac{3}{4} \quad \frac{3}{5} \quad \frac{3}{7} \quad \frac{3}{8} \cdots$$
$$\frac{4}{1} \quad \frac{4}{3} \quad \frac{4}{5} \quad \frac{4}{7} \quad \frac{4}{9} \quad \frac{4}{11} \cdots$$

At this point we might stop for a moment and see, with this much of a hint, whether we can now order the rationals in such a way that every one will be paired with a unique natural number and whether we will be able to count with the natural numbers to any rational we choose, such as $\frac{2}{3}$...

Cantor's way was to order them diagonally, beginning in the upper lefthand corner with $\frac{1}{1}$.

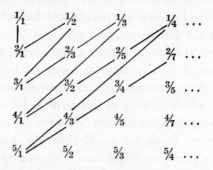

Thus we have all the rationals placed in one-to-one correspondence with the natural numbers and we quite promptly get to $\frac{2}{3}$.

$$
\begin{array}{cccccccccc}
0 & 1 & 2 & 3 & 4 & 5 & 6 & 7 & 8 & 9 \cdots \\
\updownarrow & \updownarrow & \updownarrow & \updownarrow & \updownarrow & \updownarrow & \updownarrow & \updownarrow & \updownarrow & \updownarrow \\
\frac{1}{1} & \frac{2}{1} & \frac{1}{2} & \frac{3}{1} & \frac{2}{3} & \frac{1}{3} & \frac{4}{1} & \frac{3}{2} & \frac{2}{5} & \frac{1}{4} \cdots
\end{array}
$$

This is mere child's play compared to the task of arranging the algebraic numbers so that they too can be placed in one-to-one correspondence with the natural numbers. The algebraic numbers are all those numbers which are roots of algebraic equations of the form

$$a_0 x^n + a_1 x^{n-1} + \ldots + a_{n-1} x + a_n = 0$$

in which the coefficients $a_0, a_1, \ldots, a_n$ are all integers. This is nothing more than the general expression for the algebraic equations with which we are familiar where n has a value of 1 or 2. When $n = 1$, we have a simple equation like $2x - 1 = 0$, where we can see at a glance that the root, or value of x, must be $\frac{1}{2}$. When $n = 2$, we have a familiar quadratic equation like $3x^2 + 4x + 1 = 0$, where the root, or value of x, is -1. The essential thing for us to remember is that when such an algebraic equation has whole number coefficients, as in our examples, it *always* has a root among the complex numbers. (This is the Fundamental Theorem of Algebra, proved by Gauss.) Those complex numbers which can be roots of such algebraic equations are called the *algebraic numbers*. They are not, as we shall see, all of the complex numbers by any means.

Cantor's proof that these algebraic numbers can be placed in one-to-one correspondence with the natural numbers has been called "a triumph of ingenuity"; yet it is essentially as simple as the alphabetization of the telephone book. The crux of the method is what Cantor called the *height* of an algebraic equation. This is the sum of the absolute values of the coefficients plus the degree of the equation less 1. (The absolute values are the numerical values of the coefficients with no attention paid to whether they are positive or negative; the degree is the highest power of the unknown x, or the value for n in the general expression as given above.) Thus the equation of the third degree

$$3x^3 - 4x^2 + 5x - 5 = 0$$

has a height of 19, since $3 + 4 + 5 + 5 + (3 - 1) = 19$.

Having assigned for every algebraic equation a method of determining its height as an integer, Cantor proved that for any integer there is only a finite number of equations which have that particular integer for their height. From this point on, the method of the phone book comes in handy. When we have ordered all algebraic equations according to their height, we find that in most cases we have more than one equation of a particular height. Undaunted, we arrange the equations of the same height according to the value of their first coefficient and where the first coefficient is the same, according to the second, and so on. Since there is only a finite number of equations with the same height, and since no two equations can have exactly the same coefficients, we have assigned every algebraic equation to a unique position in an order arrangement.

Our purpose, however, is not to order the equations but to order the numbers which can be their roots—the *algebraic numbers*—so that they can be placed in one-to-one correspondence with the natural numbers. So we continue by taking the roots of the ordered equations, which may be more than one but are never more than the degree of the equation, and arrange them according to their increasing value, first according to the value of the real part and then, where several numbers have the same real part, according to the value of the imaginary part. By agreement, as in the case of the rational numbers, we throw out those which re repetitions. We now have a method by which every number which can be the root of an algebraic equation can be paired with one of the natural numbers—this in spite of the fact that we have not actually written down the roots of a single equation!

Cantor's "triumph of ingenuity" can be best appreciated when we recall our diagram of the complex number plane as formed by axes of the pure imaginary and of the real numbers and recall that, although the algebraic numbers are not all the numbers upon the plane, they are everywhere dense upon it, while the natural numbers mark only the units on one-half of the real number axis! Yet these two seemingly unequal classes have the same cardinal number, $\aleph_0$.

Is $\aleph_0$ the *only* transfinite cardinal?

We are beginning to suspect that perhaps it is. We have examined many infinite classes of numbers which represent certain specific points upon the complex number plane. All of them are, of course, sub-classes of the complex numbers. Some are sub-classes of the natural numbers as well, and some include the natural numbers as one of their sub-classes. Yet always we have found (with Cantor) that the classes we have examined can be ordered in such a way that they can be placed in one-to-one correspondence with the natural numbers and, therefore, have the same transfinite cardinal, $\aleph_0$.

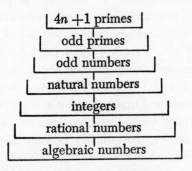

Although we can define infinite classes as being equal, it seems that we cannot define them as being greater or less. Perhaps we were right to begin with: an infinite number is just an infinite number. Fortunately, we were wrong. If we were right, the infinite would be an infinitely less interesting subject than it is. There *is* a transfinite cardinal greater than $\aleph_0$—there is, in fact, an infinite number of greater transfinite cardinals! But at the moment we shall be satisfied with only one. We can find an infinity which is greater than the infinity of natural numbers on a very small part of the real number line: the segment between 0 and 1.

To show that these real numbers, which are the equivalent of all the points on the segment, cannot be placed in one-to-one correspondence with the natural numbers, Cantor began by *assuming* that they could be. This is a method of mathematical proof as old as Euclid, who used it to show that the number of primes is infinite. It was also used by Fermat to show that all primes of the form $4n + 1$ can be expressed as the sum of two squares. The method of *reductio ad absurdum* is "one of a mathematician's finest weapons," in the words of G. H. Hardy (1877-1947). "It is a far finer gambit than a chess gambit: a chess player may offer the sacrifice of a pawn or even a piece, but a mathematician offers *the game*." In this case, to prove that the placing of the real numbers in one-to-one correspondence with the natural numbers was impossible, Cantor risked assuming that such a pairing was indeed possible.

All of the numbers on the segment of the real number line between 0 and 1 can be represented as never ending decimal fractions, and this is the way in which Cantor chose to represent them. If, however, we start to write down the actual decimals we immediately become involved in all sorts of difficulties. The first would be 0.000000000 . . . with the 0's continuing to infinity; but what would be the second decimal? No matter how many 0's we place between our decimal point and our first positive place value, we can always construct a smaller decimal by inserting one more 0 and moving our first positive place value over one more place to the right.

0.0000000000000000000000000000000000000001...

but

0.00000000000000000000000000000000000000001...

Have we proved, then, that it is impossible to arrange the real numbers from 0 to 1 in such a way that they can be placed in one-to-one correspondence with the natural numbers? No. We have proved nothing of the kind. Only that we have not been able to find a way of doing what we want to do. The question then becomes not whether we can find a way, but whether there *is* a way.

To prove that there *isn't* a way, we begin by assuming that there *is*. We solve the problem of determining the second decimal and all succeeding decimals by assuming that they have been determined. We then think of them abstractly as expressions like $0.a_1a_2a_3a_4a_5a_6a_7\ldots$ with each a_n denoting the particular value (0,1,2,3,4,5,6,7,8, or 9) of each place in the decimal; and we place them in one-to-one correspondence with the natural numbers, in accordance with our assumption that they can be so placed.

$$
\begin{array}{ll}
0 & 0.a_1a_2a_3a_4a_5a_6a_7a_8a_9\ldots \\
1 & 0.b_1b_2b_3b_4b_5b_6b_7b_8b_9\ldots \\
2 & 0.c_1c_2c_3c_4c_5c_6c_7c_8c_9\ldots \\
3 & 0.d_1d_2d_3d_4d_5d_6d_7d_8d_9\ldots \\
\ldots & \ldots
\end{array}
$$

Cantor showed that such an assumption was false because, even assuming that all decimals could be and had been placed in one-to-one correspondence with the natural numbers, he could construct a decimal which had not been included in the class of "all" decimals so ordered. This decimal he indicated by

$$0.m_1m_2m_3m_4m_5m_6m_7m_8\ldots,$$

m_1 being any digit (except 9)* other than the digit represented by a_1 in the first decimal; m_2 being any digit (except 9) represented by b_2 in the second decimal; and so on. This new decimal would be one not included in the original class of "all" decimals because it would differ from every included decimal in at least one place: from the first in at least its first place, from the second in at least its second place, and so on.

We can see a little more vividly what Cantor did if we take a concrete set of decimals and then by following his method construct a decimal not in our set.

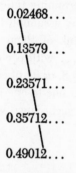

0.02468...

0.13579...

0.23571...

0.35712...

0.49012...

To get a decimal not in the set, we make the first place of our new decimal different from 0; the second, from 3; the third, from 5; and so on. It will differ in at least one place from any decimal in the set: 0.14623... is not included, and there are many other possibilities.

It is almost impossible to overestimate the importance of this achievement. Already Cantor had shown that the attribute *equal* was applicable to infinities; now he showed that the attributes *greater* and *less* were also applicable.

* Since terminating decimals like .25 can be represented as non-terminating decimals in two ways: either as .250000 . . . or as .249999 . . . , we exclude 9 to avoid having our new decimal a different representation of a number which has already, in a different form, been included in the class of "all" decimals.

The new cardinal number, which is easily shown to be larger than t $\aleph_0$, the cardinal number of a "countable" infinity, is $\mathfrak{c}$, the number of what Cantor called the continuum—an "uncountable" infinity!

What other infinities have this same $\mathfrak{c}$ as their cardinal number?

The answer to this question is completely contrary to intuition. We have noted that the real numbers from 0 to 1 are equivalent to the points on the segment of the real number line from 0 to 1, just as all the real numbers are the equivalent of all the points on the line. Our intuition tells us that the infinity of real numbers must be greater than the infinity of real numbers between 0 and 1, just as the infinity of points on the line must be greater than the infinity of points on the line segment between 0 and 1. Yet it is very easy to prove that for every point on the long line there is a point on the short line and that, therefore, there are as many real numbers between 0 and 1 as there are in all the length of the real number line!

To prove this statement, we shall take two lines (one short, which we shall call *AB*, and one somewhat longer, which we shall call *CD*) and place them parallel to one another. We shall then construct one line which passes

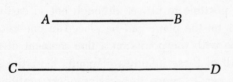

through *A* and *C* and another line which passes through *B* and *D*. The intersection of these two lines we shall call *O*. It is clear that we can draw a line from *O* to any point *Q* which we choose on line *CD*, and that this line *OQ* will of necessity intersect line *AB* at some point *P*. Therefore, for

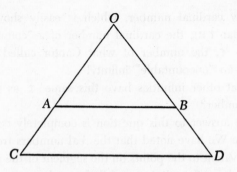

every point *Q* on the longer line there will be a unique point *P* on the shorter line which can be placed in one-to-one correspondence with it.

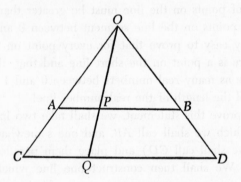

It is also possible to prove, although not so easily, that all the points on the plane can be placed in one-to-one correspondence with the points on a line segment of any finite length. All of these infinities of points have the same cardinal number, $\mathfrak{c}$. Since the real numbers represent all the points on the line, and the complex numbers all the points on the plane, they also have $\mathfrak{c}$ as their cardinal number.

Now that we have distinguished between two types of infinities, those which, like the natural numbers, are "countable" and those which, like the real numbers, are "uncountable," we might think that we were finished with the subject of the infinite. But the infinite is not so easily disposed of.

There are an infinite number of transfinite cardinals which are greater than c, which is greater than $\aleph_0$.

This important fact in the arithmetic of the infinite is stated by a very simple theorem to the effect that

$$2^n \text{ is always greater than } n$$

and supported by a very simple proof. If we consider this theorem when n is a finite cardinal number, we can see that it is true. We take n blocks—n in this case being equal to 3—and paint each block either blue or red. The number of possible color schemes will equal 2^n, or $2^3 = 8$ in this case.

1	2	3
B	B	B
B	B	R
B	R	B
B	R	R
R	B	B
R	B	R
R	R	B
R	R	R

As here, when n is a finite cardinal, we can actually count the color schemes and can actually see that we have exhausted the possibilities: no one can turn up with another color scheme for three blocks painted either red or blue which is not already among the color schemes we have.

But now let us take $n = \aleph_0$. Let us take as many blocks as we have positive integers. Again, let us paint each block either blue or red. How many possible color schemes can we have? Certainly an infinite number. For instance, we could in each case paint the nth block blue and all the others red.

1   First block blue and all others red.
2   Second block blue and all others red.
3   Third block blue and all others red.
. . .

Obviously this is too easy. After we have paired a unique color scheme with every one of the positive integers, we can think up one or an infinity more of schemes which we have not included. For instance, we could paint the nth and the $(n + 1)^{th}$ block blue and all the others red, and this would give us a completely different set of color schemes which could also be placed in one-to-one correspondence with the positive integers. But remember that even another infinity of color schemes does not prove that both sets of color schemes could not be placed in one-to-one correspondence with the positive integers, or even all possible color schemes!

So let us assume that by some method we have determined all possible color schemes and to each block we have attached one of the color schemes. *Now* can we come up with a color scheme which is not among those attached to the blocks? We can and we do—using the same method by which we constructed a decimal which was not in our original set of "all" decimals. We pick up the first block and note from the color scheme attached to it what color it is to be painted in that particular scheme. Then we paint it a different color, red if it was blue on the list, blue if it was red. The color scheme which results from our newly painted blocks cannot possibly be one of those already attached—or paired in one-to-one correspondence—to the blocks. It will differ, for at least one block, from each of the color schemes we already have. The cardinal number, then, of all possible color schemes is greater than the cardinal number of the blocks because the color schemes cannot be placed in one-to-one correspondence with the blocks. Our theorem—2^n is greater than n—is true whether n is finite or transfinite.

It follows, therefore, that for any transfinite number there is always another and greater transfinite number. There is no *last* transfinite number. The number of transfinite cardinals is infinite!

Of this infinitude of transfinite numbers, $\aleph_0$, as its subscript indicates, is the first. What is $\aleph_1$? The cardinal number of the continuum, c, is larger than $\aleph_0$. There is no known transfinite number that is smaller than c and larger than $\aleph_0$. But is c the second transfinite number? Is it $\aleph_1$? [*]

In modern mathematics this problem holds the place that the problem of the trisection of the angle held in ancient mathematics. We have indeed counted the infinite, *but we are not done with it!*

[*] That c is $\aleph_1$ is the famous "continuum hypothesis."

6

"Nothing, Intricately Drawn Nowhere"

The subject of geometry is almost synonymous with the name of Euclid. For this reason, when we first hear of something called non-Euclidean geometry, we feel that there is some misunderstanding. Why, Euclid *is* geometry! But our trouble is only in our tenses. Euclid *was* geometry for more than two thousand years. He isn't any more.

The story of how Euclid was deposed, and at the same time elevated, is one of the longest, in many ways the most ironic, and without question one of the most important in the history of mathematics.

As we recall from our high school geometry, Euclid deduced all of his theorems, or propositions as they were sometimes labeled, from a relatively small set of definitions and basic assumptions, called, more or less interchangeably, *axioms* or *postulates*. For a very long time it was believed that these assumptions of Euclid's, which we have printed in full on the opposite page, were true, in the ordinary way of what we mean by "true"; and because they were true, the theorems which were logically deduced from them were "true" in the same ordinary way.

AXIOMS AND POSTULATES OF EUCLID *

Axioms

1. Things which are equal to the same thing are also equal to one another.

2. If equals be added to equals, the wholes are equal.

3. If equals be subtracted from equals, the remainders are equal.

4. Things which coincide with one another are equal to one another.

5. The whole is greater than the part.

Postulates

Let the following be postulated:

1. To draw a straight line from any point to any point.

2. To produce a finite straight line continuously in a straight line.

3. To describe a circle with any center and distance.

4. That all right angles are equal to one another.

5. That if a straight line falling on two straight lines makes the interior angles on the same side less than two right angles, the straight lines, if produced indefinitely, will meet on that side on which the angles are less than two right angles.

Yet geometry is a subject whose "truth" is immediately controverted by its very name. *Geometry* means *earth-measurement,* and that was an accurate name for the art which the Greeks learned from the Egyptians. On the small

* This version is given by Sir Thomas Heath in *The Elements of Euclid.*

part of the earth which was flooded each year by the Nile, the Egyptians found it necessary to develop a system of measurement by which they could reestablish boundary lines after each inundation. But let us take a globe—for the earth itself, as we shall see, is for various reasons too large for our purposes—and let us take a few of the "truths" which the Egyptians arrived at from experience and which the Greeks deduced in logical fashion from their axioms and postulates.

A straight line is the shortest distance between two points.

The sum of the angles of a triangle is 180°.

The circumference of a circle is $2\pi r$.

These ideas of straight lines, triangles and circles are almost as familiar as our own faces. We all know, for instance, what a straight line is. It is the shortest distance between two points, and it is, well, *straight*. But when we try to draw a straight line on the surface of the globe, it is immediately apparent that we can't draw any sort of line which even begins to meet our intuitive idea of what a straight line should be. Obviously (it is not at all obvious, but we think it is!), we can stretch a thread across the surface of the globe between any two points, say San Francisco and London, and find the shortest distance between them. Since "the shortest distance between two points" satisfies part of our definition, we can call the line marked by the thread a *straight* line if we will just forget what we usually mean by *straight*. If we extend the line which marks the shortest distance between San Francisco and London all the way around the globe, we find that it divides the surface into two equal parts. In other words, it is a great circle. The great circle with which we are most familiar is the one we call the equator. Although arcs of these great circles are the straight line segments of our surface—being the shortest distance between two points—our idea of straightness is violated by calling them such, and so we call them the *geodesics* of the surface. The geodesics of the Euclidean plane, or a perfectly flat surface like a floor, are what we call "straight lines."

Since we cannot draw "straight" lines on our globe, we cannot have straight-sided triangles. Our triangles will bulge on the sides and in the center. If we take one such triangle, flatten it with as little distortion as possible onto this page, and then join its vertices with straight lines, we see at a glance that if the sum of the angles of the interior triangle is 180°, as we know by Euclidean geometry that it is, the sum of the angles of the spherical triangle must be more than 180°.

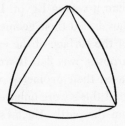

We have seen that the shortest distance between two points on the globe is not a straight line, that the sum of the angles of a triangle on the globe is not 180°. Now let us draw a circle on our globe. It meets exactly the Euclidean definition of a circle as "the locus of points equidistant from a center," and we may jump to the conclusion that all we know about a Euclidean circle will also be true of such a circle. But the interior of this circle does not look like the interior of the circle we know about. It is two-dimensional, but it is not flat. It may look, depending on how large it is and how large is the globe upon which it is drawn, like a ball cut in half or a hub cap or merely a saucer. If we place it on this page and trace around its edge, we shall have a flat circle. Of this circle we know that the circumference is twice the product of π and the radius. But obviously the curved circle drawn on the surface of the globe, which must have had the same circumference, cannot have had the same radius. Its radius must have been greater because of the curvature of the surface on which it was drawn. Its circumference, therefore, cannot be equal to $2\pi r$.

Although geometry means earth-measurement, it is apparent that the measurement of the earth has very little to do with the geometry of the Euclidean plane. This was not because the Greeks of Euclid's time (300 years before Christ) did not know that the earth was round. They had calculated that it was, from the fact that the North Star was higher in Greece than it was in Egypt. But the geometrical figures on which they based their geometry were drawn on only a small part of the surface of the earth, and that part, for all practical purposes, was flat. It would be more exact to say that they based their geometry on idealized figures on an ideal plane, and these were only represented by those which they drew on the earth. Euclid's geometry was indeed, as Edna St. Vincent Millay has written, "nothing, intricately drawn nowhere."

Yet for two thousand years, in spite of the fact that the geometry of Euclid did not truly apply to the only large surface which man knew and had not constructed himself, it was felt that this geometry—then the *only* geometry—represented "truth," in so far as man could know it. One philosopher (Kant) called the ideas from which Euclid deduced his theorems "the immutable truths"; another (Mill) considered them "experimental facts." Mapmakers and sailors might struggle with the geometry of the boundless, finite surface that is our planet; but Euclid's geometry, extended to three dimensions and a space which was thought both boundless and infinite, was the geometry of God's mind.

That the geometry of Euclid was not the only one possible, either physically or mathematically; that it was deduced not from self-evident truths but from arbitrarily chosen and unprovable assumptions; that another choice of assumptions could yield a geometry just as consistent, just as useful and just as true, never occurred to anyone for more than two thousand years unless, in a sense, it had occurred to Euclid himself when he set out the assumptions on which he based his geometry. For today it is clear that Euclid recognized what no other man between his time and that of Gauss recognized: that his axioms and postulates were assumptions which could not be proved.

The idea of those who followed Euclid and extolled him was that the axioms and postulates of his geometry did not have to be proved because they were self-evident. There was only one impediment to the full and complete acceptance of this point of view and that was the fifth postulate, which makes a statement very roughly equivalent to our common statement that parallel lines never meet. From the beginning, compared to the other axioms and postulates, this one did not seem quite self-evident enough, even to the most devoted admirers of the master.

The famous fifth postulate stated as follows:

If a straight line falling on two straight lines makes the interior angles on the same side less than two right angles, the two straight lines, if produced indefinitely, will meet on that side on which the angles are less than two right angles.

As J. L. Coolidge has remarked in his *History of Geo-*

metrical Methods, ". . . whatever else this postulate may be, self-evident it is not."

The fifth postulate makes a statement about the entire length of a straight line, a statement which can never by its nature be verified by experiment. To remove this flaw from the work of the master, generation after generation of mathematicians attempted to prove the statement about parallel lines from the other postulates. Time after time they failed: they were never able to prove the fifth postulate without substituting for it still another postulate, which simply varied the problem rather than solving it.

Among the last of the attempts to "free Euclid from every flaw" was one made by a Jesuit priest, Geronimo Saccheri (1667-1733). It was Saccheri's idea that although the parallel postulate did not, on the surface, seem as self-evident as the others, he could show that it was the only possible assumption because any other "led to absurdity." This, as we have seen, is an ancient and honorable method of mathematical proof. We assume the falsity of that which we wish to prove true, or the truth of that which we wish to prove false, and then show that such an assumption is unfeasible because it leads us to a contradiction; hence follows the truth of whatever we were trying to prove in the first place. Saccheri's method was mathematically sound; the only thing which was not sound was his attitude. When he found that assumptions about parallel lines quite different from the famous "fifth" did not lead him into the expected contradictions but into a strange and fantastic geometry which was nevertheless as consistent as Euclid's, he fell back upon his feelings instead of his brains and peppered the last pages of his work with such epithets of the logically defeated as "destroys itself," "absolutely false," "repugnant." Great discoverers have made great mistakes. Columbus found the new world and thought that it was the old. Saccheri found a new world and refused to disembark because he thought he knew that there could be only one world.

It was a century after Saccheri that three mathematicians in three different countries,[*] independently and apparently without knowledge of Saccheri's curious contact with non-Euclidean space, came to the conclusion that Euclid had known exactly what he was doing when he made his statement about parallels a postulate instead of a theorem. He had recognized what no one else had recognized: that it was completely independent of the other postulates and therefore could not possibly be deduced from them.

To prove this suspected independence of the "fifth," it was necessary only to substitute for Euclid's assumption about parallels a contrary assumption and then to show that the geometry deduced from it, in conjunction with the other postulates and axioms of Euclid, was as consistent as Euclidean geometry itself. The word *consistent* in the last sentence may stop some of us—and it should—for it is the word upon which the whole idea of Euclidean and non-Euclidean geometries turns. It is desirable that the axioms from which we deduce a set of theorems be simple, somehow significant in that they lead to interesting theorems, and independent of each other so that there is no unnecessary repetition among them. All of these are in the nature of artistic requirements. This does not mean that they are not important, for real mathematics is essentially beautiful and sets for itself the same standards as any work of art: simplicity, seriousness and economy. The artistic requirements for a set of axioms are mathematically important, but they are not indispensable. The one indispensable require-

[*] Nikolas Ivanovitch Lobatchewsky, Russia; János Bolyai, Hungary; and Gauss, Germany.

ment, without which any set of axioms no matter how beautiful is completely unacceptable, is that of consistency. A set of axioms must never lead us to a contradiction: we must not be able to deduce from the same set of axioms that A is equal to B and also that A is not equal to B.

It is natural to ask how we know that a given set of axioms will never lead to a contradiction. This is a question which, naturally, has occurred to mathematicians too. David Hilbert (1862-1943), who was the mathematicians' mathematician during the era in which Einstein was the newspapers' mathematician, devoted the greatest effort of his career to establishing the over-all consistency of mathematics by proving the absolute consistency of any one set of axioms. Kurt Gödel (1906-   ), whom many would call the greatest mathematician alive today, demolished Hilbert's project with the sort of finality which, among the sciences, is almost unique in mathematics. It is—unless some human error in logic has passed undetected—as final as death. Gödel *proved* that the proof of the absolute consistency of any set of axioms is, in a word, impossible.*

How then do we justify a statement that a non-Euclidean geometry is as consistent as Euclidean geometry? Obviously, bearing in mind Gödel's proof, we cannot claim that the axioms of Euclidean geometry will never lead to a contradiction. We can say only that they never have. For all practical purposes, then, we can use Euclidean geometry as a standard of consistency among geometries. Later we shall see the way in which a non-Euclidean geometry can be placed against this standard and found to measure up to it.

* The consistency of a system of axioms cannot be established within the system but must be referred to another system, the consistency of which can only be established by reference to *another* system, and so on.

The first of the non-Euclidean geometries was, in the relation its axioms bore to those of Euclid, the simplest possible. All the axioms were exactly the same except one, the famous "flaw," the long worked-over statement about parallels. We have noted that this parallel postulate may be stated in various ways, all equivalent in the sense that the same set of theorems can be deduced from any of the various versions. The statement which appears in the set of axioms on page 81 is the earliest known; but since even the earliest known manuscripts of Euclid's *Elements* date from a time nearly a thousand years after the death of Euclid, the master himself may have stated the parallel postulate in a somewhat different form. It is clear from the theorems, however, that some statement of like nature must have existed among the original set of axioms. The most easily grasped statement is a later one, known as the Postulate of the Unique Parallel:

Through any point not on a given line, one and only one *line can be drawn which will never meet the given line.*

Now let us make a contrary assumption and let us change the postulate to read:

Through any point not on a given line, infinitely many *lines can be drawn which will never meet the given line.*

Before our intuition objects to the postulate in this new form, let us recall that on the globe, where the equivalent of a straight line is a great circle, it is impossible to draw through a given point *even one line* which will never meet a given line, since every great circle intersects every other great circle. A word of caution, though. We mention the contrary example that on a sphere every straight line— or geodesic of the surface—intersects every other straight line, only to put intuition in its proper place. Mathematically, it has nothing whatsoever to do with whether the alternate above is a proper postulate. When a set of axioms more or less agrees with our idea of reality, we will deduce from that set of axioms a geometry which also agrees pretty well with the same idea of reality. This does not mean that our idea of reality is right, but only that our axioms agree well enough with whatever reality there is so that the geometry deduced from them works. We have seen that the earth is not the infinite plane of Euclidean geometry; yet small parts of it are, for all practical purposes, very much like small parts of the plane; and so for building pyramids and super-markets it works very well indeed. But we shall also see that the non-Euclidean geometries, which attempted to show only from an intellectual point of view that it was possible to deduce geometries as consistent as Euclid's from a different set of assumptions, turned out to have quite a bit to do with reality, too.

The first non-Euclidean geometry, based on the same set of assumptions as the old (except for the new Postulate of Infinitely Many Parallels for the old Postulate of the Unique Parallel), applies to a surface which is the direct opposite of the surface of any part of the sphere. The surface of the sphere is what we intuitively think of as "evenly curved"; in mathematics this is more precisely defined as "constant positive curvature." The surface to which our first invented non-Euclidean geometry applies is one of "constant negative curvature." It is not (probably fortunately) a very common one in the physical world; but we can dredge up examples of such a surface: a saddle, for instance, or a mountain pass or the surface around the hole of a doughnut. In these, however, the negative curvature is only local. For a surface of constant negative curvature, we can look ahead to the illustration on page 92.

If we place a plane tangent to a single point on a surface of constant negative curvature, like a portion of a saddle, we find that it cuts the rest of the surface in two hyperbolas. For this reason the earliest non-Euclidean geometry, which applies to such a surface of negative curvature, is called *hyperbolic* geometry. If we place a plane tangent to a single point on a surface of constant positive curvature, like a portion of the sphere, and then shift the plane ever so slightly so that it is parallel to its original tangent position, we find that it cuts the surface in the shape of an ellipse. (In the special case of the sphere, it will cut a circle, which is a special case of an ellipse.) For this reason a later non-Euclidean geometry, which applies to such a surface of positive curvature, is called *elliptic* geometry. It substitutes for the Postulate of the Unique Parallel the following statement:

Through any point not on a given line, no line *can be drawn which will not intersect the given line.*

From our earlier experiments with our globe, we recognize that on the surface of a sphere, where a straight line is a great circle, the above postulate holds. For our purposes in this chapter, a sphere can serve as an example of a surface of elliptic geometry. Actually it is what is called "locally elliptic." To make the entire surface elliptic, a curious change must be made. As we recall, the purpose of non-Euclidean geometries is to establish the fact that geometries as consistent as Euclid's can be deduced with a different parallel postulate, the others remaining the same. It is an axiom of Euclidean geometry that two straight lines can intersect at only one point, but on the sphere two great circles always intersect at two points. To get around this difficulty, in elliptic geometry we *identify* the two points of intersection as one point. Although in this respect the geometry of the surface of the sphere as a whole is not technically elliptic and non-Euclidean, it is locally; and we can take a sphere as our sample elliptic surface.

The true surface of hyperbolic geometry—not just a portion but an entire surface—is what is called the pseudosphere, a sort of doomsday world of two unending trumpets.

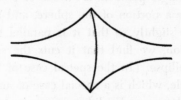

Let us now compare in a few simple respects the "truth" of certain geometrical statements in relation to the plane, the sphere and this pseudosphere. Straight lines, which are "straight" on the plane, follow the surface and therefore curve out on the sphere, curve in on the pseudosphere. Triangles on the sphere curve out; on the pseudosphere, in; and circles appear, depending on the surface, like saucers or limp watches. What happens to geometric "truths"? They are no longer true-false statements, but multiple-choice. The sum of the angles of a triangle is (equal to, more than, less than) 180°. The circumference of a circle is (equal to, more than, less than) $2\pi r$. Through a point not on a given line (one, none, infinitely many) lines can be drawn which will never meet the given line. Which is "true"?

When we compare the geometries of these three very different surfaces, we see that the geometry of one surface cannot be applied to another. We see also that of these three, the surface of the sphere is the one which we can say with greatest accuracy "exists" for us. Yet portions, if not too large, of the imperfect sphere on which we live are more like portions of the Euclidean plane. On the Pacific

Ocean we might choose the geometry of the sphere, but in our own backyard we'll take Euclid. So far no one in everyday life has found the geometry of the pseudosphere indispensable; nevertheless, logically it is one with the others.

It is interesting to note at this point that if we did not know the nature of the surface of our "earth" we could discover whether the curvature was positive or negative—always provided that it was not too large—in several different ways. Perhaps the simplest would be by adding up the angles of a fairly large triangle. If they added up to definitely more than 180° we would know that we were living on a surface of positive curvature; if to definitely less than 180°, that we had our existence on a surface of negative curvature. But it would be practically impossible to determine with finality that our "earth" was a boundless, endless Euclidean plane. We could never go far enough out so that we could state that the plane was infinite, and we could not even say definitely that it was a plane, or a surface of curvature 0. Whether the total degrees of the three angles of a triangle was exactly 180°, slightly more or slightly less, the range of experimental error would prevent our knowing for sure that it was flat. If, however, our surface is sufficiently large, whether the curvature as a whole is positive, negative or exactly zero, we will find Euclidean geometry most practical because any portion of the surface with which we are concerned will seem, for all practical purposes, flat.

Non-Euclidean geometries were invented not to provide geometries for unusual surfaces but to show that from assumptions other than Euclid's (specifically, a different postulate about parallels) equally *consistent* geometries could be deduced. One of the ways of establishing this consistency is by identifying the objects and relations of Euclidean geometry with certain other objects and relations which result in a non-Euclidean geometry. All of the facts of Euclidean geometry then apply to the model of the non-Euclidean geometry with the exception of the Postulate of the Unique Parallel which, in the case of hyperbolic non-Euclidean geometry, is replaced by the Postulate of Infinitely Many Parallels. It follows, therefore, from the model that the non-Euclidean is as consistent at least as Euclidean geometry.

One of the best-known models of hyperbolic non-Euclidean geometry is that of Felix Klein (1849-1925). In this model the plane of Euclidean geometry is defined as the points of the interior of a circle. Each of these points is defined as a non-Euclidean point, and the chords of the circle are defined as non-Euclidean straight lines. Other definitions are made, but these three will be sufficient to explain the model below where, as we can see, through a given point P not on a straight line AB, infinitely many straight lines can be drawn which will never intersect the given line.

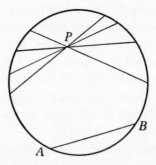

The invention of non-Euclidean geometry had very much the same effect on mathematics as the invention of non-commutative algebra, which it actually preceded by a few years. Both freed mathematics from the tyranny of the "obvious," the "self-evident" and the "true," and in so doing served to reveal the nature of mathematics as well as the nature of algebra and geometry. With the invention of non-Euclidean geometry, it was recognized for the first time that the theorems of a geometry are logically deduced from a set of arbitrarily chosen assumptions. The truth of the geometry is determined within this framework and has nothing to do with the "truth" (as judged by external facts) of the assumptions from which it is deduced.

We are inclined to think of a geometry as being tailored, as it were, to fit a particular surface; but actually geometries are rather like ready-made suits. They can be used if they fit. Euclidean geometry fits portions of the earth very well, although the idealized type of surface which is implicit in the geometry apparently does not exist at all—"nothing, intricately drawn nowhere." The surface of elliptic non-Euclidean geometry on which we go halfway around and come back to our starting point, and the surface of hyperbolic non-Euclidean geometry on which the "ends" of the world become smaller and smaller as they approach infinity are as non-existent as the Euclidean plane. The fact has nothing to do with their mathematical importance. They were not invented to be useful.

It is important that we clearly understand this point, for something happened sometime after their invention which gave to these non-Euclidean geometries the same kind of physical importance that was for so many centuries the unique possession of Euclidean geometry. Just as the algebra for quantum mechanics was discovered in a non-commutative algebra (long on the books as "useless" in a practical sense but "useful" in a mathematical sense), so the geometry for relativity was discovered in a non-Euclidean geometry of boundless, finite, "curved" space. In such a space the geodesics are paths of light waves, which are deflected in varying degrees from their "straight" course by the various masses in space. It is easy to glimpse from just the brief examination we have made of the geodesics of plane, sphere and pseudosphere the implications such deflection would have for any geometry of space.

Mathematically, the usefulness of non-Euclidean geometry was a bonus over and above its mathematical usefulness, which was, as we have seen, the freeing of mathematics from its ancient bonds.

The new freedom, which included freedom from the axioms of Euclid, did not, however, include dispensing with Euclid's axiomatic method. This had been the ideal of all mathematicians since his time. Yet actually it had been hobbled by the definition of an axiom as a self-evident truth. When this definition was dispensed with and an axiom recognized as simply an arbitrary assumption, the axiomatic method became infinitely more valuable to mathematics.

So it is that while Euclid is no longer all geometry, he *is* the axiomatic method—the logical ideal and aim of mathematics and of all science—and the "flaw" which so many generations of mathematicians labored to remove from the work of the master is seen as no flaw at all, but the hallmark of his genius.

7

No Such Thing as "the" Fourth Dimension

The common method of mapping by coordinates, which enables us to find our way about an unfamiliar part of our city, enables mathematicians to move mentally in a world of *n* dimensions with as much freedom as they move physically in a world of three.

The application of the method of coordinate mapping to geometry and algebra, which is called in the history of mathematics *the invention of analytic geometry,* was one of those innovations which, as soon as they are finally made, seem inevitable. It freed both subjects from bonds which had until then seemed inherent in them. As geometrical figures were transformed into algebraic equations and equations into figures, whole new worlds were opened up to mathematics. Of all these, the world of *n* dimensions beckons most alluringly to us who are firmly imbedded in three!

The first step into this world is taken when we select

an arbitrary point on the plane and label it, in the way of mathematicians, O for "origin." It does not matter which point we select to start from, for the plane extends from any point in all directions "to infinity." So for convenience we shall put O in the middle of this page, and it is from here that we shall begin our curious journey.

. O

Through O we draw a line which extends indefinitely to the right and to the left. On this line we mark off units very much as years are marked off from an origin point which is the birth of Christ. The units "after," or to the right of O, are labeled with a plus; the units "before," or to the left, with a minus. We then draw, perpendicular to our first line, another which passes through O and extends indefinitely above and below it. On this line we mark off units, as degrees of temperature are marked off on a thermometer: the units "above" O being labeled with a plus and the units "below" with a minus. Our original horizontal line we call the x-axis; this new vertical line which is perpendicular to it, the y-axis.

On the plane we can now locate uniquely any point, any line of finite or infinite length, any plane figure or any plane surface. To give the position of a point, we find the number x which tells its distance from the y-axis and the number y which tells its distance from the x-axis. On the diagram below, consider the four points which are indicated as number pairs.

We not only can think of these points as number pairs but also handle them as number pairs. They are no longer geometrical points; they are things of arithmetic. This works both ways. We can think of any pair of numbers as a unique point in the plane. The briefest glance tells us in which

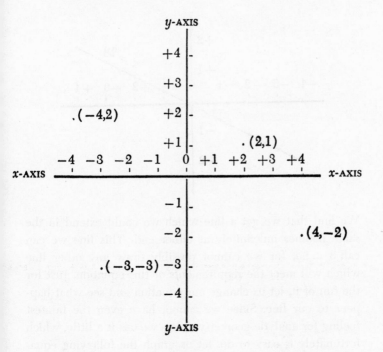

quadrant it belongs; the slightest effort pin-points it—no longer a number pair but a point, a thing of geometry.

A point, we say then, is an ordered pair of numbers (x,y). When we know the values for x and y, we know where the point lies on the plane. But what happens when the values of x and y change continuously as the point moves about the plane leaving in its trail a path which we call a line? Let us say that in one case all we know about these changing values is that the value of x is always twice the value of y, and let us locate some such points on the plane and join them.

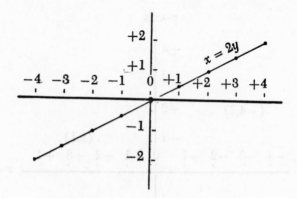

We find that we get a line which we could extend in the same manner indefinitely at either end. This line we can call $x = 2y$, for we cannot possibly draw any other line which will meet the requirements of this equation. Just for the fun of it, let us change our equation and see what happens to our line. Since we cannot have even the faintest feeling for analytic geometry unless we use it a little, which fortunately is easy to do, let us graph the following equations, the first few points of which are already indicated.

$$x = y \ (1,1),(2,2), \ldots$$
$$x - y = 2 \ (2,0),(3,1), \ldots$$
$$4x + 3y = 18 \ (0,6),(1,14/3), \ldots$$

All three of these equations can be expressed in the standard form of the equation of the first degree in two unknowns: $ax + by + c = 0$. This form of expressing any equation so that the right side is 0 was originated by René Descartes (1596-1650), who invented analytic geometry.* Under this arrangement, the equations which we

---

* It was Descartes who also started the custom of using the last letters of the alphabet for the unknowns and the first for the constants, as we have done above in the general equation for a straight line.

graphed above become $x - y = 0$, $x - y - 2 = 0$, and $4x + 3y - 18 = 0$.

The reader who enjoyed graphing the three equations above will be interested to see what happens when he graphs the following equations, a few points of which we have indicated as before.

$$y = x^2 \quad (1,1), \ (\pm 2,4), \ \ldots$$

$$xy = 4 \quad (1,4), \ (-\frac{1}{2},-8), \ \ldots$$

$$x^2 + y^2 = 4 \quad (0, \pm 2), \ (-1, \pm\sqrt{3}), \ \ldots$$

In this simple system of coordinates by which points, lines and figures can be presented algebraically or be used to represent algebraic equations, we have all the basic concepts we need for our promised trip into space of n dimensions.

The idea of dimensionality has been with mathematics since the time of the Greeks. The lengthless breadthless point traced out a line, which had one dimension. The line traced out a plane, which then had two dimensions; the plane traced out a space, which then had three dimensions. No one with a human desire for consistency could follow this process and fail to ask the next question. Why not a figure, a sort of hypersolid, traced out by a solid moving in a 4-dimensional space? But a 4-*dimensional* space! What could it possibly be like?

Let us try, in fancy, to put ourselves in the place of "people" in a 2-dimensional world and see, as it were, through their eyes how impossible it would be for them to "visualize" our 3-dimensional world or even, for that matter, to see a 3-dimensional object which passed through their world.* A sphere, for instance, passing through the

* Such people and such a world are the subject of *Flatland, a Romance of Many Dimensions* by Edwin A. Abbott.

plane, would be seen by the inhabitants of the plane as successive circles growing first larger and then smaller. But we cannot truly project ourselves into a 2-dimensional world because all the time we know that the sphere is there. Like the audience in a thriller, we want to yell, "Look!" We can't believe that there is anyone who wants to yell "Look!" at us.

Although we cannot visualize a 4-dimensional space, we can visualize the effect that "going into the fourth dimension," as science fiction writers say, would have on an object from space of three dimensions. This also we come to by a logical extension of what we can actually see of the relation between space and the plane. Let us take a piece of paper, trace out the soles of our shoes, and cut them out. We have a right sole and a left sole, mirror images of each other. If we limit ourselves to sliding them around in the plane, on a table top, for instance, we can never make them both left soles. But if we lift the right sole off the table (out of the plane and into space), we can turn it over so that it is a left sole when we return it to its mate. Now let us take the shoes, one right and one left, from which we traced the soles. These are 3-dimensional objects in 3-dimensional space. We know from experience that we can never turn the right shoe into a left shoe. But if we were able to lift it out of our space and into a 4-dimensional space, turn it over and return it, *what would have happened to it?*

There is yet another way by which we can get a visual idea of 4-dimensional space. This too is by a logical extension from the three dimensions with which we are familiar. Let us take the simplest figures in each dimension:

A line segment is bounded by two points.

A triangle is bounded by three line segments.

A tetrahedron is bounded by four triangles.

Should there not be, in a 4-dimensional space, a figure

bounded by five tetrahedra? This logical extension of the first three figures we call a pentahedroid. When the five tetrahedra are regular, the pentahedroid (it can be proved) is one of the six regular bodies possible in a 4-dimensional space.

What does the pentahedroid look like? Well, it is a figure bounded by five tetrahedra. Although we are somewhat like the Lady of Shalott in that we cannot turn and see it and live, we can look at it in several of the ways in which we are accustomed to looking at 3-dimensional figures. For instance, we can dismantle it, as if it were a Tibetan monastery being prepared for shipment to the home of an American millionaire, the pieces carefully labeled so that they can be put together again in another land. Then we shall actually have seen a 4-dimensional body—in pieces. But we can also see it in a manner similar to one in which we are accustomed to seeing three dimensions in two. We are familiar with the real appearance of objects in photographs and paintings. Of course, it is our actual experience with the object in three dimensions which for us gives a reality to its representation in two, and this actual experience is not possible in four dimensions. Nevertheless, we can construct a perspective model in three dimensions of a never-seen and never-to-be-seen but *logically thought out* figure in four dimensions.

We can give an example which is so simple as to be trivial and yet illustrates exactly the relationship. If we are drawing several cubes and are looking at one of them from a position directly in front of it and level with it, we see only—and draw only—the square face of the side of the cube which is toward us. In this particular case a square is a 2-dimensional representation of the 3-dimensional cube. In an equivalent 3-dimensional representation of a 4-dimensional hypercube we have before us—because our projection of the hypercube into our space is "head on"—a cube, which is one of the faces of the hypercube. In the comparable projection of the cube, one face of the cube (or a square) was behind the face we saw and the other four faces had been projected into the four straight lines bounding the face we saw. When we look at the cube, which is the head-on projection of the hypercube, there is behind the cube another cube which we cannot see, just as we could not see the square behind the square; and each face of the cube that we can see is a projection of a bounding cube, comparable to the projection of planes into lines in the projection of a cube into a square.

It is, of course, impossible to construct an actual model of a 4-dimensional figure, but mentally we are not so limited. If we do not insist upon an answer to our very human question, "But what does it actually look like?", we can think freely of objects in space of any number of dimensions or, as the mathematicians say, n-dimensional space where n is any number greater than 3.

After our excursion through what might be called the sideshows of dimension theory, let us go back to the system of coordinate axes on which we were mapping the points, lines, figures and surfaces of 2-dimensional space. We saw that any point on the plane could be uniquely located by a number pair (x,y); but also that any point in space could be uniquely located if only we had a third axis. This, the z-axis, we erect at O perpendicular to the plane formed by the x and y axes. Now instead of two coordinates, x and y, to locate a point, we need a third, z.

To see how this extension of the system of coordinate mapping works, let us consider the points in the illustration on page 99. On the plane they are uniquely identified by their x and y coordinates as $(2,1)$, $(-4,2)$, $(-3,-3)$, $(4,-2)$. If we raise the first two points one unit above the plane and lower the last two points one unit below the plane, we get $(2,1,1)$ and $(-4,2,1)$ above the plane and $(-3,-3,-1)$ and $(4,-2,-1)$ below the plane. If we raise each of the four original points a different amount, the first one unit, the second two, and so on, we get the points $(2,1,1)$, $(-4,2,2,)$, $(-3,-3,3)$ and $(4,-2,4)$, each one a unique point and each one uniquely identified.

Following the general method we have already outlined, we can locate points, lines, plane figures and solids in 3-dimensional space. The only difference is that instead of expressing these by equations of two variables we shall need equations of three variables. The equation $ax + by + cz + d = 0$ represents a plane in 3-dimensional space just as the equation $ax + by + c = 0$ represents a line in 2-dimensional space.

It is only natural at this point that we ask what is represented by an equation in *four* variables? We do not have to be mathematicians to guess the answer to this one. If an equation of the first degree in two variables represents a line in 2-dimensional space, an equation in three variables represents a plane in 3-dimensional space, then an equation in four variables represents a space (or hyperplane) in 4-dimensional space, and so on.

The reason that we are able to move so freely in *n*-dimensional space is that, thanks to analytic geometry, we no longer have any need to visualize what we are talking about. We are just talking about algebraic equations. But do not make the mistake of thinking that the geometry of *n* dimensions is all algebra after $n = 3$. There is a division of labor. Algebra does the work, and geometry suggests the ideas. If, for instance, in 2-dimensional space we have a number pair (x,y) and another pair (x',y'), geometry suggests that we can use in our algebra the concept of "the distance" between (x,y) and (x',y'), since any given number pair can always be represented as a unique point in the plane. The way in which we do this is as old as geometry itself. If we draw a line from (x,y) parallel to the y-axis and a line from $(x'y')$ parallel to the x-axis, the two lines will intersect. When we join (x,y) and (x',y') we have a familiar figure.

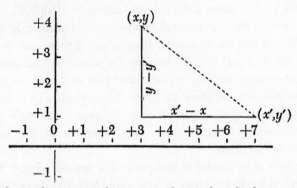

By the Pythagorean Theorem we know that the hypotenuse of the right triangle, which is also the distance between our two points, is the square root of the sum of the squares of the two sides. We say, then, that our distance formula for two ordered pairs of numbers (x,y) and (x',y') is the one below.*

$$d^2 = (x - x')^2 + (y - y')^2$$

In the specific case of the two points above $(3,4)$ and $(7,1)$, the formula gives us $(7 - 3)^2 + (4 - 1)^2 = 25$. The square root of 25 being 5, this is the desired distance between the two points.

When we put our points in a 3-dimensional space as number triples (x,y,z) and (x',y',z'), we have the same formula for the distance between the two points except that we have a third variable, z and z'.

$$d^2 = (x - x')^2 + (y - y')^2 + (z - z')^2$$

* Note that the result of squaring $(x-x')$ is the same as the result of squaring $(x'-x)$.

We can apply this formula in the following concrete problem. We wish to determine the distance from the back right-hand corner of the top of our desk to the bottom of the front left-hand leg. To do this, we determine first the length of the diagonal of the top of the desk. Then, with this as one side of our right triangle and the front left-hand leg as the other, we determine the length of the hypotenuse, which is the desired distance. Try it with a desk.

It is not just the abstract concepts of geometry—like that of distance—which suggest ideas to algebra. Even the geometric figures of space of four dimensions, which we found impossible to visualize a few pages back, become mere formulas and lead us to extensions of themselves in higher and higher dimensions. We are all familiar with the circle and its extension into three dimensions, the sphere. If we map a circle on the plane with its center at the origin, the formula for its radius is

$$x^2 + y^2 = R^2,$$

and this means simply that the square of the radius is the sum of the squares of the x and y coordinates of any point on the circumference. That this is true can be seen from the figure below, where again we meet the Pythagorean

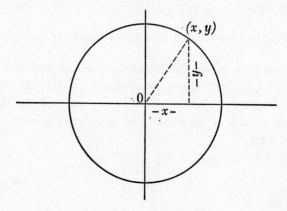

Theorem. "It runs," E. T. Bell has written, "like a golden thread through all of mathematics."

Just as we extended the distance formula into dimensions higher than 2, we can extend the formula for the radius of a circle to the radius of a sphere, a hypersphere, and so on.

$$x^2 + y^2 = R^2$$
$$x^2 + y^2 + z^2 = R^2$$
$$x^2 + y^2 + z^2 + w^2 = R^2$$

We must not think that the mathematics of n dimensions is nothing more than adding another letter for each dimension that we add. Things that are mathematically interesting begin almost as soon as we add that next letter, and they are not at all predictable. If they were, the mathematics of n dimensions might be very useful—which it is—but it would not be very interesting—and it is.

Although the extension of the formula for the radius of the circle into three and four dimensions was made in routine fashion, the extension of the formula for the area of the circle into higher dimensions is not nearly so routine:

For the area of a circle, $\qquad\qquad A = \pi r^2.$

For the volume of a sphere, $\qquad\qquad V = \dfrac{4}{3}\pi r^3.$

For the hypervolume of a hypersphere, $H = \dfrac{1}{2}\pi^2 r^4.$

Here we have a very interesting and unexpected relationship. Two generalizations are involved and they alternate, depending upon whether the dimensionality of the figure is even or odd. If the number of dimensions is even, $n = 2k$, we have

$$\frac{\pi^k r^{2k}}{k!}$$

but if the number of dimensions is odd, $n = 2k + 1$, the general expression is quite different.

$$\frac{2^{2k+1}k!\pi^k r^{2k+1}}{(2k + 1)!}$$

As we go farther into the geometry of n dimensions, we find that we never know at just what n our extension may become suddenly more difficult. Consider the problem of packing spheres into space so that in some regular pattern we can fit in the greatest number of spheres. For $n = 2$ we get the most circles on the plane by alternating staggered rows.

For $n = 3$ we arrange each layer of spheres in the same way that we arranged the circles but stagger the alternate layers. We can continue in similar ways, although it is not at all easy to prove, through $n = 8$. At $n = 9$, the problem inexplicably takes a more difficult turn. At the present time there is no one who can tell us how to pack 9-dimensional spheres in 9-dimensional space.

The geometry of n-dimensions might just as well be called the algebra of n variables, but either way the intellectual journey which begins at O on the cartesian plane takes us through fascinating if purely mental country, and never ends!

8

Where Is In and Where Is Out?

When, as very young children, we are told to copy a drawing of a triangle, we produce a blob. If we are then given a neat little square to copy, we produce a brotherly blob. A long thin rectangle is transformed into a blob, and so is a circle.

As far as we are concerned, the blob is a reasonable reproduction of any number of simple geometric figures. It is generally admitted that we do not draw very well. Yet we have perceived the essential likeness of all the figures we have been given to copy, a likeness which will escape us in later life when a rectangle, for instance, will seem like something entirely different from a circle.

The fundamental similarity of triangle, square, rectangle and circle is that they all divide the plane (or the piece of paper on which they are drawn) into two distinct and mutually exclusive parts: that part A, which is inside the boundary, and that part B, which is outside. A point C which is in A cannot simultaneously be in B. For C to move from A to B, it must cross the boundary of the figure we have drawn, whether it be triangle, square, rectangle or circle. If we think of each of these figures as drawn on a thin sheet of rubber, we can see that no matter how we pull the sheet about, so long as we do not cut or tear it, we shall never be able to affect in any way this basic and common characteristic.

If, however, we take certain figures like those below which divide the plane, or the paper on which they are drawn, into more than two parts, we shall find that no amount of stretching will turn them into the figures we were first concerned with.

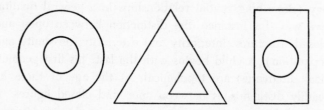

Yet, although we cannot reduce any of these figures to our first simple blobs, we can reduce each of them to a blob with a blob cut out of it; and this is the way, as children, we would have drawn any one of them.

Recalling the straightedge and compass of high school geometry, the protractor in its envelope at the back of the book, the painstaking care with which we drew each figure and lettered the appropriate points, we find it hard to believe that this casual approach to figures can be geometry too. Yet it is. Topology, as this geometry is called, is one of the newest, the most all-inclusive and the most abstruse branches of mathematics. It concerns itself with the truly fundamental properties of geometrical figures, surfaces and spaces. Most of its problems are so removed from our everyday experience that it is impossible for us even to glimpse them, let alone grasp them; yet, as in the higher arithmetic, some of its most difficult problems can be stated in the language of a child.

This is not as surprising as it might at first seem. In an article entitled "How Children Form Mathematical Concepts" (*Scientific American*), Jean Piaget has written:

"A child's order of development in geometry seems to reverse the order of historical discovery. Scientific geometry began with the Euclidean system (concerned with figures, angles and so on), developed in the 17th century the so-called projective geometry (dealing with problems of perspective), and finally came in the 19th century to topology (describing spatial relationships in a general qualitative way—for instance, the distinction between open and closed structures, interiority and exteriority, proximity and separation). A child begins with the last: his first geometrical discoveries are topological. At the age of three he readily distinguishes between open and closed figures: if you ask him to copy a square or a triangle, he draws a closed circle; he draws a cross with two separate lines. If you show him a drawing of a large circle with a small circle inside, he is quite capable of reproducing this relationship, and he can also draw a small circle outside or attached to the edge of the large one. All this he can do before he can draw a rectangle . . . Not until a considerable time after he has mastered topological relationships does he begin to develop his notions of Euclidean and projective geometry. Then he builds those simultaneously."

Yet the only formal geometries with which most adults are familiar are these last two!

In that with which we are most familiar—the Euclidean geometry we were taught in high school—we studied and proved statements which established the likenesses among different types of figures—triangles, for instance. We were especially fond of the right triangle. Following in the footsteps of Pythagoras, we found that the square constructed on the hypotenuse of the right triangle was equal to the sum of the squares on the other two sides and that all right triangles, regardless of their sizes and shapes, were alike in this respect. (We have seen how this ancient theorem runs through all mathematics: arithmetic, algebra and analysis as well as geometry—we even meet it, in a modified form, in the mathematics of relativity; but one place we never meet it is in topology!)

The other geometry with which we may also have become familiar in high school, in the art course, since it is not taught as mathematics at that level, is projective geometry. (It was Cayley who exclaimed, "Projective geometry is all geometry!"—but it is not topology.) Here, when we attempted to draw the corner of a room, we discovered a curious thing. The corner was formed by the meeting of three right angles and we knew by Euclidean geometry that a right angle is 90° and that the sum of three right angles must be 270°; but when we drew the corner on paper, so that it looked to the eye exactly like the corner we saw, the sum of the three right angles was always 360°! *
Mathematically, this mystery is explained by the statement that the size of an angle is invariant under rigid motion but not under projection.

Invariants under rigid motion—length, angle, area—are

* This, of course, is because the corner when projected to the plane on which we are drawing it must fill an entire circle, or 360°.

the subject of Euclidean geometry. Invariants under projection—point, line, incidence, cross-ratio—are the subject of projective geometry. (Rigid motions are technically a class of projections.) No matter how we slide a right triangle about on the plane, we never affect its "triangleness" nor its "rightness"; but when we draw it from differing points of view, although we retain its "triangleness," we lose its "rightness." The transformations of topology, which include rigid motions and projections as special classes, are in general much more drastic. Under the particular group known as the deformations, a right triangle can be transformed into any other type of triangle, a polygon of any number of sides more than three, an ellipse, a circle and so on. Yet, through all these changes the characteristic which we perceived when we drew our first triangle as a blob will remain invariant: it will divide the plane into two distinct and mutually exclusive parts, an inside and an outside. This characteristic is invariant under deformation for any figure like the triangle which topologists classify as a *simple closed curve*.

Although intuitively we have an idea of what we mean by a simple closed curve, let us arm ourselves with a more precise definition. When we think of a curve we probably think of something the opposite of sharp, angular, straight; but in mathematics the sharp, the angular and the straight may all be curves. The ancient definition of a curve is that it is the path traced by a moving point. In the spirit of this definition, a closed curve is one whose end point is the same as its beginning point; and a simple curve is one which does not pass through the same point more than once. It is obvious from this definition that circles, triangles, rectangles and higher polygons, as well as blobs, are all simple closed curves. It is not quite so obvious that the figure at the top of the next page is a simple closed curve.

What we perceived so early in life about simple closed curves—that they divide the piece of paper on which they are drawn into an inside and an outside—is one of the fundamental theorems of topology.

Theorem: A simple closed curve in the plane divides the plane into exactly two domains.

There are many mathematical theorems which, in the course of this book, we will receive with puzzled frowns or raised eyebrows; but the Jordan Curve Theorem, as the above is known, is not one of them. This theorem was first stated by Camille Jordan (1838-1922). Besides being a mathematician of the first order, Jordan was a great teacher and the author of a textbook, *Cours d'analyse,* which is an acknowledged masterpiece. In *A Mathematician's Apology* Hardy has stated his own debt to Jordan and to his book as follows:

"I shall never forget the astonishment with which I read that remarkable work, the first inspiration for so many mathematicians of my generation, and learnt for the first time as I read it what mathematics really meant. From that time onwards I was in my way a real mathematician, with sound mathematical ambitions and a genuine passion for mathematics."

We have included this testimonial from Hardy to make clear that Jordan was a mathematician of stature and influence. If Jordan was interested in the fact that a simple closed curve divides the plane into two domains, it must be more interesting and less obvious than the observation of a three-year-old would lead us to believe. (Actually modern mathematicians have a considerable respect for the obvious. They have found that quite often what appears obvious is not at all, in fact quite often it is not even true. They have also found that even when it is true, it is often almost impossible to prove that it is true.) Jordan experienced considerable difficulty in trying to prove the obvious theorem which bears his name, so much difficulty that his proof did not meet the rigorous standards which he himself had set up in his *Cours d'analyse*. Time and effort on the part of other mathematicians finally filled the logical gaps in his reasoning. When at last it was completely acceptable from the rigorous point of view, the proof of this "obvious" theorem was nothing for children. It was so extremely technical that even mathematicians found difficulty in following it.

Why should it be so difficult to prove what we have shown is readily apparent even to a three-year-old?

The answer to this question lies in the complete generality of Jordan's theorem. It is simple (relatively) to prove it for any special case of curve. For instance, we can give a simple method for determining whether a given point is inside or outside the labyrinthine "simple closed curve" that we drew on page 115. Incidentally, the reader can first determine that this is, indeed, a simple closed curve by tracing it. He will find that without lifting his pencil and without crossing a line he can go around the entire curve and return to his starting point. It is a little harder to determine whether a given point is inside or outside. To do so, we take a direction which is not parallel to any side of the figure. Although sometimes difficult, this is not impossible, since any straight-edged closed curve has only a finite num-

ber of sides and hence of directions. To determine whether
a given point is inside or outside the curve, we direct a
"ray" in the chosen direction from the point and past the
curve. If the ray crosses the boundary an even number of
times, the point is outside; if an odd number of times, inside. Below we have applied this method to a fairly simple
figure, but the reader should also apply it to the figure on
page 115 too.

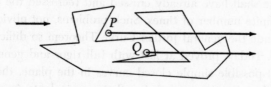

The general problem—in other words, the proof in respect to all simple closed curves—presents difficulties which
do not occur in the special case of straight-edged closed
curves. *All* simple closed curves include, in addition to the
various examples we have already mentioned, such curiosities as curves which have area, curves to which no tangent
can be drawn, curves which cross and recross a straight line
infinitely many times within an arbitrarily small distance.
Although these are contrary to all we think we know about
curves, they too may be simple closed curves; and when
we make a statement about simple closed curves, as we do
in the Jordan Curve Theorem, we are making a statement
which must be shown to apply also to such curious curves!

The greatest difficulty of all in proving this theorem is
one which seems at first preposterous. *Where is in and
where is out?* It is very easy to show that there exists at
least one point which is outside the curve. Knowing that
the plane is infinite in extent, we select a point sufficiently
far away from the boundary so that it is unquestion-

ably outside. But how do we go about showing that there is at least one point which is inside the curve? In the case of the ordinary everyday simple closed curve, the kind which makes the Jordan Curve Theorem seem so obvious, we find our inside point by selecting one which is on the other side of, and an arbitrarily small distance from, the boundary. Even mathematicians agree that such a point is inside. But this method will not be of any use to us when, in going even an arbitrarily small distance across the boundary we shall have already crossed and recrossed the curve an infinite number of times. Such problems, not obvious at all, made the general Jordan Curve Theorem so difficult to prove. Today, proved at last with full rigor and generality for all possible simple closed curves in the plane, the theorem has been extended for their equivalents in space. These are the simple closed surfaces like the sphere and the polyhedra which divide space into two distinct and mutually exclusive parts, that which is inside them and that which is outside.

We again imagine these figures to be made of rubber, thin enough to be stretched at will into any topologically equivalent shape we choose yet strong enough to hold a shape. As we pull them about, what other characteristics about them remain invariant? No matter how we stretch these surfaces, we cannot change the fact that each has two sides, an inner side and an outer side. We also cannot change the fact that they have no edge. These, like the characteristic of dividing space into two parts, are invariant.

If we puncture our general balloon-like surface and carefully stretch it out flat, we get a surface which we can call a disk. This disk, which we can say is the topological equivalent of a sphere with one hole in it, does not of course divide space into two parts because it encloses no space. It is not unbounded, as the sphere is, and therefore it has an edge where the sphere has none. It has, however, one characteristic of the sphere. It has two sides. Unless we are somewhat informed on the subject of topological curiosities, we may think that all surfaces have two sides, and if this is all the sphere and the disk have in common, it isn't much. However, although it is impossible to have a three-sided surface, it is perfectly possible to have a surface with only one side.

We can take our disk, with its two sides and its one edge, and stretch it out into a long thin strip like the one below.

Let us paint one side of this strip red, and one side green. Then let us pick it up and join the two ends so that red meets red and green, green. We have a band which is red on one side and green on the other. Like the strip (from the disk) with which it was formed, it has two sides; but unlike the strip, it has not one edge but two. The original strip was the topological equivalent of a sphere with one hole in it; the band is the topological equivalent of a sphere with two holes in it.

Now let us take another similar but unpainted strip and give it a half twist before we join the ends together. We do not have a band, but something quite different topologically. Where the band has two sides and two edges, the Möbius strip, as it is called, after A. F. Möbius (1790-1868), has only one side and one edge. If we attempt to paint one side red, we shall never find a place to stop until we get back to where we started, and by then the entire strip will have been painted red!

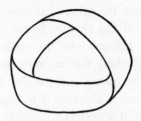

The Möbius strip and the band were both made from a strip which was a stretched-out disk; yet no amount of stretching will enable us to make a Möbius strip into a band or a band into a Möbius strip. What happens, though, when we perform a similar operation upon all three? We cut them down the length. The original strip falls into two strips; the band falls into two bands; but the Möbius strip remains in a single piece! (Try cutting it again.)

Topologists, it is clear, look at things and see them differently from the way most of us do. Where we see a circle or a triangle or a square, a topologist sees a simple closed curve; where we see a knot—just a knot—a topologist sees many different kinds of knots, and he is fascinated by them.

By a knot, a topologist means nothing so simple as even the most complicated knot that boy scout, first-aid instructor, cowboy or sailor can tie. A knot which is tied can be untied. It is, therefore, topologically equivalent to the piece of string or rope out of which it was tied, a line segment or a simple open curve. A topologist is interested in knots which are not tied and therefore cannot be untied. Such knots are essentially loops or circles, simple closed curves in space, but with a difference.

The most famous of these is probably the trefoil, or clover leaf, knot pictured below in two different forms.

No amount of stretching or pulling or clever weaving can transform one of these knots into the other. Yet both (in fact, *any* knot) can be mapped upon a simple closed curve, a rubber band, for instance. We put the band and the string out of which the knot is made together at one point and then keep them together at each point as we move around the rubber band. Eventually we come back to where we started, never having had to separate string and rubber band at any point. In this respect a knot is equivalent to a simple closed curve; yet no amount of stretching, nothing short of cutting the knot and rejoining the ends, can make a knot into a simple closed curve, for it is imbedded in three-dimensional space in a different way.

We may think of knots only as pleasant puzzles, yet they present topology with one of its greatest unsolved problems: that of classifying different kinds of knots according to their invariants. One method which works very well for the great majority of knots is that of associating each one with a certain surface, the edges of which can be arranged so that they trace out that particular knot. A Möbius strip with three half twists instead of the usual one, for instance, will trace out in the path of its edge a trefoil knot.

But a *general* method of classification which would cover all cases has not yet been discovered.

Here, as in the proving of the Jordan Curve Theorem, the difficulty lies in the complete generality of the problem: yet if a general method of classifying knots can be found, much in related topological fields will fall automatically into place, like minor candidates riding into office on the leading candidate's coattails.

Perhaps the solution to this problem lies within the future grasp of some chubby hand drawing circles and triangles as indistinguishable blobs.

"One thing seems certain," wrote E. T. Bell in *The Development of Mathematics:* "to think topologically, the thinker must begin young. The cradle with its enchained teething rings may be a little too early; but the education of a prospective topologist should not in any case be deferred beyond the third year. Chinese and Japanese puzzles of the most exasperating kind, also the most devilish meshes of intertwisted wires to be taken apart without a single false move, should be the only toys allowed after the young topologist has learned to walk."

Topology is one of the youngest branches of an ancient

subject, and much of its strength has come from the youth-fulness with which it has looked at age-old figures. It has seen what was always there but never seen before—by grownups.

9

How Big? How Steep? How Fast?

How big?

How steep?

How fast?

Among these three apparently unrelated questions
there exists a deep and unexpected point of contact which
can serve us as an introduction to the calculus, one of the
most powerful tools of mathematics. It is by means of the
calculus that mathematics has been able to make an effec-
tive attack on those problems which in earlier times admitted only of approximate answers.

Invented in the seventeenth century by Sir Isaac Newton (1642-1727) and Gottfried Wilhelm Leibnitz (1646-
1716), who worked independently, the calculus had had
its beginnings long before in two purely geometrical problems: how to compute an area bounded by a curve and
how to draw a tangent to a curve at any point. More than
nineteen hundred years before either of the inventors of the
calculus was born, Archimedes (B.C.287?-212), using what

were essentially its methods, solved for special types of curves both of these problems.

How big?

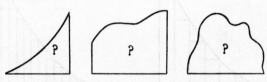

The question *How big?* was one of the first to which mathematics sought an answer, and one of the first to which it found one, although not for all cases. Given a rectangular area, it is a simple matter to compute that area as a sum of unit squares or, as we more often express it, the product of length and width. Given a triangular area, it can be shown that the area of a triangle is half that of a rectangle with the same base (width) and height (length) or, again, as we more often express it, one-half the product of base and height. Since any straight-edged surface, no matter how irregular its boundary, can be subdivided into triangles, the only remaining problem is to find the area bounded in part or in whole by a curve.

One method of doing so is to divide the area insofar as possible into rectangles and add together the areas of these. In the first figure below, it is clear that the sum of the areas of the rectangles, which we can compute exactly, will give us a fair approximation. In the second, it is clear that more rectangles give an even more accurate approximation of the area which lies under the curve. We can continue, indefinitely, dividing the area into more and more rectangles and including as a result more and more of the total area under the curve. When we say that we can continue indefinitely, this is just what we mean: there is no limit to the number of rectangles into which we can divide the area—the number can "approach infinity." There is, how-

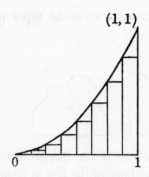

(1, 1)

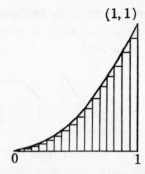

(1, 1)

ever, a very real limit to the sum of the areas, no matter how many rectangles: *for it can never exceed the area under the curve.*

This limit provides us with a mathematically precise definition of what we mean by the area under the curve. It is the limiting value of the sum of the areas of the rectangles as the number of rectangles becomes indefinitely large.

Is this a satisfactorily accurate method of determining area? It is indeed. How very accurate it is can best be seen by applying it, not to a curved figure, the exact area of which we do not already know, but to a straight-edged figure like a triangle, the area of which we know is ½*BH*.

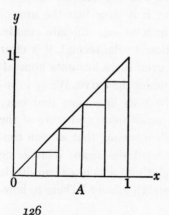

A

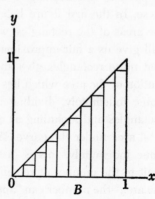

B

By this formula the area of the triangle above is exactly ½. Since the y coordinate of any point on the hypotenuse has the same value as the x coordinate, we can easily determine the dimensions of each rectangle. In Fig. A, where we have divided the triangle into five intervals, the width of each being ⅕ of the base, we get the following sum when we add the areas together.

$$\frac{1}{5} \cdot \frac{0}{5} + \frac{1}{5} \cdot \frac{1}{5} + \frac{1}{5} \cdot \frac{2}{5} + \frac{1}{5} \cdot \frac{3}{5} + \frac{1}{5} \cdot \frac{4}{5} = \frac{10}{25}$$

But in Fig. B, where we have divided the base into tenths, we get a sum which is even closer to ½, the true area of the triangle.

$$\frac{1}{10} \cdot \frac{0}{10} + \frac{1}{10} \cdot \frac{1}{10} + \frac{1}{10} \cdot \frac{2}{10} + \cdots + \frac{1}{10} \cdot \frac{9}{10} = \frac{45}{100}$$

By increasing the number of intervals from 5 to 10, we have brought our approximation from .40 to .45. The area with 50 intervals would be .49; with 100 intervals, .495. If we take n as the number of rectangular intervals into which we divide the triangle, we obtain the following general formula for the sum of the areas of n rectangles.

$$\frac{1}{n}\left(\frac{0}{n} + \frac{1}{n} + \frac{2}{n} + \cdots + \frac{n-1}{n}\right) =$$
$$\frac{1}{n^2}\left(0 + 1 + 2 + \cdots + n-1\right) =$$
$$\frac{1}{n^2}\left[\frac{n(n-1)}{2}\right]$$

If the reader, using this formula, will compute the sum of the areas of five hundred and one thousand rectangular intervals, he will find that these and any other higher n he chooses to compute will yield sums *between* .495 and .50. Under no circumstances will the sum of the rectangles into which he divides the triangle be more than .50. That this is true is intuitively clear when we look at the triangle being subdivided and note the tiny triangles above the tops of the rectangles which can never be included in the sum of the areas. It is also clear when we further simplify our general formula for the sum of the areas.

$$\frac{1}{n^2}\left[\frac{n(n-1)}{2}\right] =$$

$$\frac{1}{2}\left(\frac{n-1}{n}\right) =$$

$$\frac{1}{2}\left(1-\frac{1}{n}\right)$$

As n gets larger (i.e., we cut our triangle into more and finer rectangles), $1/n$ gets smaller. As this happens, the value of

$$\frac{1}{2}\left(1-\frac{1}{n}\right)$$

will approach ½, the actual area.*

This method of determining area Archimedes called the method of "exhaustion" and Newton and Leibnitz, "integration." The latter two were fortunate in having at their disposal a tool which was not available to Archimedes. This was the analytic geometry of Descartes, with which—as has been frequently pointed out—a moderately intelligent boy of seventeen can solve problems which baffled the greatest of the Greeks. This statement is made, not to discredit Archimedes, whose place with Newton and Gauss in the pantheon of mathematics is universally acknowledged, but

* We can achieve the same result by circumscribing our rectangles so that they include all the area of the triangle. As the number of rectangles gets larger, the sum will approach from the other side the limit which is the area of the triangle.

only to emphasize the power of the method of analytic geometry. When we can place our curves and figures on the plane formed by the x and y axes, we have a great advantage over Archimedes.

Curves, for instance, are no longer merely beautiful lines but definite relationships among numbers which can be expressed in a most general form—for the whole extent of the curve—by algebraic formulas. The straight line, or "curve," which forms the hypotenuse of the right triangle on the lower part of page 126 is determined by the algebraic equation $y = x$. When we say this, we mean that the numerical value of the y coordinate at any point on the curve is the same as the numerical value of the x coordinate at that point. If we are given $x = 9$ at a given point, we know that $y = 9$; if $x = 21$, $y = 21$; and so on. The curve on the upper part of page 126 is determined by the equation $y = x^2$. On this curve the numerical value of the y coordinate is always the square of the value of the x coordinate: if $x = 3$, $y = 9$; if $x = 9$, $y = 81$; and so on.

This method of analytic geometry is even more useful in answering our second question than it was in answering the first.

How steep?

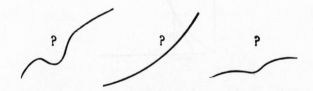

The question *How steep?*, like the question *How big?*, is simple enough to answer when only straight lines like $y = x$ are involved. If we look at the line below, we see that one measure of its steepness is the angle it makes with the x-axis and another is the ratio between the two coordinates x and y. If we take y/x as a measure of steepness, we see from the second figure that the greater y is in proportion to x, the steeper the line.

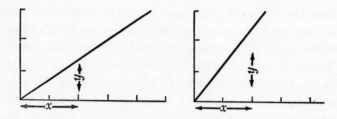

Neither method appears to be available to us when we want to determine the steepness of the parabola, or the curve represented by the equation $y = x^2$. Yet if we could draw a line which would have the same slope as the curve at some particular point, the same two methods of measuring steepness would serve.

Although the problem of determining such a line was solved by Archimedes in the special case of the spiral, it was not solved generally for all curves until, in the century before Newton and Leibnitz, Fermat developed a general method of drawing a line (called a tangent) which touched a curve at only one point and hence had the same slope as the curve at that point.

When our curve is the arc of a circle, a line erected perpendicular to the radius at the point where it cuts the circumference will be tangent to the circle at that point. If we place the circle on the cartesian plane with its center at the origin, the lines constructed perpendicular to the y-axis at the points where it cuts the circumference will be parallel to the x-axis and will represent the highest and lowest points (or extrema) of the curve. The determination of such high and low points for any curve was the particular problem which interested Fermat and for which he created a general method for drawing tangents.

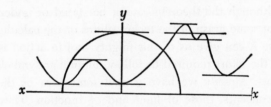

To draw a line tangent to the point P in the figure below, we mark on the curve in the neighborhood of P another point Q and draw a line from P to Q. As we slide the point on the line now marked Q along the curve toward P, always keeping the line PQ going through P, the closer Q gets to P, the more nearly will the line PQ represent the slope of the curve at P. In the language of the calculus, as Q is allowed to approach P, the line PQ will approach *a limiting position* which is the desired tangent to the curve at P.

These two geometrical problems, computing the area bounded by a curve and finding the slope of a curve at a given point, are at the very foundations of the calculus. The first is the fundamental problem of the *integral* calculus; the second, of the *differential* calculus. Both, as we have seen, were recognized from antiquity, tackled and partially solved long before the invention of the calculus in the seventeenth century. Newton and Leibnitz were the first to recognize that these two problems were but facets of one and the same problem, and that the integral and the differential calculus were essentially one—*the* calculus. The theorem which states this truly deep relationship was discovered independently by both of them. It is the Fundamental Theorem of the Calculus.

Although the theorem cannot be stated or understood without some grasp of the technicalities of the calculus, the glimpse it can give us of this mighty tool in action is well worth the effort required to follow unfamiliar symbols and concepts. Already we have gained some idea of the two main concepts, those of limit and of function. These are basic to much of mathematics beyond the calculus, and mathematicians can (and must) go on for pages defining precisely what they mean by *limit* and *function*. We, however, can make do with very little of this. We have seen that the area under the curve is defined as a limiting sum and the tangent to the curve as a limiting position. These give us an intuitive, if not too precise, idea of a limit. We have dealt with the curves of two functions so far, although we have never referred to them as functions. For our purposes, the simplest and most easily grasped definition of a function is a strictly mathematical one. A function is a rule *by which y is determined as soon as x is given*. If we apply this definition to the straight line determined by the equation $y = x$ and to the curve determined by $y = x^2$, we have no trouble in recognizing that both of these equations identify functions.

To express this concept of function there is a very simple and useful notation, $f(x)$, which is read "f of x" or "function of x." In the first of the examples we have given, $f(x) = x$; in the second, $f(x) = x^2$. Since any curve represents a value y determined by a value x at each point of the curve, we can identify any curve in a general way as $f(x)$, or as a function of x, even though we may not know the particular $f(x)$ that determines the curve.

Sometimes we are concerned not with the curve as a whole but with a particular point on the curve. Knowing that the x coordinate of the point is, say, 2, we can then write of y that $y = f(2)$. Whether y necessarily equals 2 depends solely upon the particular $f(x)$ which determines the curve as a whole. When the curve is determined by $f(x) = x$, $y = f(2) = 2$; but when the $f(x)$ of the curve is $f(x) = x^2$, then $y = f(2) = 4$.

Unfortunately, without understanding this much of the notion of function, we cannot possibly follow even the simplest applications of the calculus. Included below, therefore, are a few problems which will enable the reader to clarify and make firm his own understanding.

1. If $f(x) = x$, solve $y = f(5)$ for y.
2. If $f(x) = x^2$, solve $y = f(5)$ for y.
3. If $f(x) = x^2$, what are the y coordinates for $x = 1,2,3$?
4. If $f(x) = x$, what are the y coordinates for $x = 4,5,6$?
5. If $f(x) = 2x$, solve $y = f(8)$ for y.
6. If $f(x) = 2x-1$, solve $y = f(3)$ for y.
7. If $f(x) = 1/x$, what is the value for y when $x = 7$?
8. If $f(x) = 1-x$, what is the value for y when $x = 1$?

9. If $f(x) = x^3$, solve $y = f(2)$ for y.

10. If $f(x) = x + 3$, what is the value of y for $x = 7$?

ANSWERS: 1. $y = 5$; 2. $y = 25$; 3. $y = 1,4,9$; 4. $y = 4,5.6$; 5. $y = 16$; 6. $y = 5$; 7. $y = \frac{1}{7}$; 8. $y = 0$; 9. $y = 8$; 10. $y = 10$.

With such a general notion of limit and function, we now need an understanding of the concept of *an increment* to follow the Fundamental Theorem of the Calculus. The technique of the calculus depends essentially upon this concept. An increment is an arbitrarily small increase in x of $f(x)$ which, since $y = f(x)$, results in a corresponding (though not necessarily the same) arbitrarily small increase in the value of y. We symbolize the increment added to x by $\triangle x$ and the corresponding increment in y by $\triangle y$, and write

$$y + \triangle y = f(x + \triangle x)$$

where $\triangle$ is read "delta." To express what we have done in this general way, we do not have to know what x is, what the arbitrarily small increase in x is, what $f(x)$ is, or what the corresponding small increase in y is. We can even proceed, still not knowing the value of any of our terms, to express $\triangle y$, or the increase in y, solely in the terms of x.

$$y = f(x)$$
$$y + \triangle y = f(x + \triangle x)$$
$$\triangle y = f(x + \triangle x) - f(x)$$

Once we have expressed $\triangle y$ in terms of x, we can express the ratio $\triangle y / \triangle x$ in terms of x.

$$\frac{\triangle y}{\triangle x} = \frac{f(x + \triangle x) - f(x)}{\triangle x}$$

Perhaps we appear to be getting nowhere fast?

But it is one of the marvels of mathematics that such

apparently pointless manipulation of symbols should be the source of the power of the calculus, one of the most practical of the many tools with which mathematics has outfitted modern science! We are getting somewhere—but fast. To see that we are, let us return to the curve of the parabola, which is represented by the equation $y = x^2$. We learned earlier how to determine the slope of such a curve at any given point, but now let us consider a less geometrical and more general question. What is the rate of change represented by this curve? How fast is y changing with respect to x? Actually, although these two questions sound different, they are the same as *How steep?*

Since in the case of this curve, $f(x) = x^2$, we know that the value of y is increasing as the square of the value of x.

x	0	1	2	3	4	5	6	7 ...
y	0	1	4	9	16	25	36	49 ...

Obviously y is increasing much faster than x. Between 0 and 1, both x and y increased by 1; but between 6 and 7, x still increased by only 1 but y increased by 13. Between 0 and 7, x has gained 7 points while y has gained 49. The average gain of y in proportion to that of x is 7 to 1. But how *fast* is y gaining on x?

Let us apply the method of the calculus to this problem: a method which appeared a few pages back as a meaningless manipulation of symbols. We begin by adding an arbitrarily small amount to x in $f(x)$ so that we have instead of $f(x)$, $f(x + \triangle x)$. Since $y = f(x)$, the new value of y is $y + \triangle y = f(x + \triangle x)$. Now let us substitute for $f(x)$ in its general form the specific function x^2 with which we are dealing. We begin with

$$y = x^2.$$

After we add the increment to x^2, we have

$$y + \triangle y = (x + \triangle x)^2.$$

When we express $\triangle y$ in terms of x, we get

$$\triangle y = (x + \triangle x)^2 - x^2 = x^2 + 2x \cdot \triangle x + (\triangle x)^2 - x^2$$
$$= 2x \cdot \triangle x + (\triangle x)^2.$$

If we now express the ratio between $\triangle y$ and $\triangle x$ in the terms of x and then cancel out identical terms in numerator and denominator, we arrive at

$$\frac{\triangle y}{\triangle x} = \frac{2x \cdot \triangle x + (\triangle x)^2}{\triangle x} = 2x + \triangle x.$$

Recalling that when we first added $\triangle x$ to x in $f(x)$, we defined it as "an arbitrarily small increase," we realize that as we choose smaller and smaller amounts for $\triangle x$, i.e., $\triangle x$ approaches 0, the limiting value of the ratio $\triangle y / \triangle x$ will be $2x$. This is the rate of change of y with respect to x when $f(x) = x^2$.

We can see that $2x$ actually is the rate of change, or, to express it in a different way, the slope of the curve at a given point. We plot the parabola and then at any point draw a line the slope of which is equal to twice the value

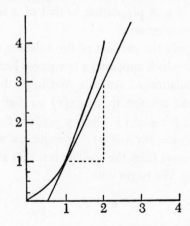

of the x coordinate of the point. For instance, at $x = 1$ the slope should be 2; so we line up our straightedge with a point 1 unit over and 2 units up from our given point on the curve. The slope of the line we draw will then be 2, and we can see that this line does represent the slope (or rate of change) of the curve at this point.

How big? How steep? How fast? We have said that there is a fundamental point of contact among these three questions. We have shown that the answers to the last two are essentially the same. *How steep? = How fast?* Now we shall show the relation of the first to these two. This has been called "one of the most astonishing things a mathematician ever discovered."

We begin by taking the area under a curve which we can identify in a general way as $f(x)$. We have seen that a curve is a function of x since each x coordinate determines a y coordinate and hence the curve itself. The area under a curve is also a function of x but in a somewhat different sense. It is clear from the diagram below that if we take a as the x coordinate of the left-hand boundary of the area we wish to compute, and b as the x coordinate of the right-hand boundary, moving b to the right on the x-axis will increase the area. In this sense the area under a curve is a function of (i.e., is determined by) the value of the x coordinate at its right-hand boundary.

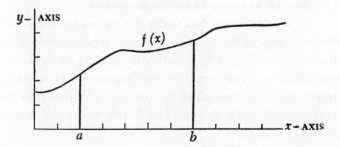

Since, although the area is also a function of x, it is not the same function as that which determines the curve above it, we represent the curve by $f(x)$ and the area by $F(x)$. This can be easily seen in the curves below. On the left we have a triangle under the curve $f(x) = x$, the value of each y coordinate being the same as that of the x coordinate of any point on the curve. If we compute the area of this triangle at each x coordinate as one-half of x^2 (or half the base times the height), we find that the curve representing the area as a function of x, or $F(x)$, is an entirely different curve.

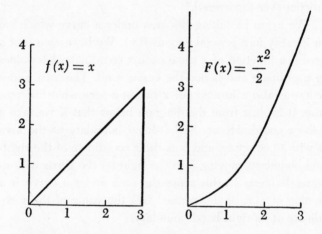

Now let us return to our main problem.

To determine the area under the curve between a and b we proceed in the by now somewhat familiar method of the calculus. We go a little farther to the right on the x-axis and add to x (represented on the diagram by b) an arbitrarily small distance which we call $\triangle x$. This results in an appropriately small increase in the area under the curve, which we call $\triangle A$.

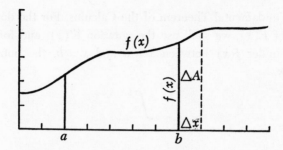

Instead of $A = F(x)$ we now have

$$A + \triangle A = F(x + \triangle x)$$

and by subtracting the original area from the enlarged area we can determine the value of $\triangle A$.

$$\triangle A = F(x + \triangle x) - F(x)$$

If we look at our diagram we can see by inspection that $\triangle A$, as well as having the value given above in terms of x, has also the *approximate* value of $\triangle x$ times $f(x)$, which would be the area of the largest rectangle we could inscribe in $\triangle A$. The ratio $\triangle A/\triangle x$ is then approximately $f(x)$.

$$\lim_{\triangle x \to 0} \frac{\triangle A}{\triangle x} = \lim_{\triangle x \to 0} \frac{\triangle x \cdot f(x)}{\triangle x} = f(x)$$

From the above we see that the area under the curve $f(x)$ is determined by a function $F(x)$ which has the property that its rate of change, or derivative as it is technically called, is $f(x)$! Since $F(x)$ answers the question *How big?* and $f(x)$ answers *How steep?* and *How fast?*, we find all three inextricably bound together. This is the fundamental relationship of the calculus.

With a brief explanation of two notations which we have not already met, we are now ready to state and follow the Fundamental Theorem of the Calculus. For the derivative of $F(x)$, we shall use the notation $F'(x)$; and for the area under $f(x)$ between $x = a$ and $x = b$, the notation below.

$$\int_a^b$$

The Fundamental Theorem, discovered independently by Newton and Leibnitz, states:

If $f(x)$ is continuous and $F'(x) = f(x)$, then

$$\int_a^b f(x)dx = F(b) - F(a).$$

Let us apply this formula to the area under the line $y = x$ between 0 and 1, which we know is $\frac{1}{2}$, and the area under the curve $y = x^2$ between 0 and 1, which we do not know. In the first case we must have a function of x, the derivative (or rate of change) of which is dx. Since we earlier determined the rate of change of x^2 as $2x$ (on page 136), we can surmise that the derivative of $\frac{1}{2}x^2$ is x. In the second case, the reader may be interested in working out (as on the same page) that the derivatives of $\frac{1}{3}x^2$ is x^2.

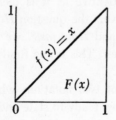
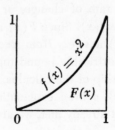

$$f(x) = x$$
$$F(x) = \frac{1}{2}x^2$$
$$a = 0, b = 1$$
$$\int_0^1 x\,dx =$$
$$\frac{1}{2} \cdot 1^2 - \frac{1}{2} \cdot 0^2 = \frac{1}{2}$$

$$f(x) = x^2$$
$$F(x) = \frac{1}{3}x^3$$
$$a = 0, b = 1$$
$$\int_0^1 x^2\,dx =$$
$$\frac{1}{3} \cdot 1^3 - \frac{1}{3} \cdot 0^3 = \frac{1}{3}$$

In the case of the triangle we know that the area is indeed ½, which the Fundamental Theorem gives us as the limit. In the case of the area under the parabola, we did not know but *now* we know that the area under the curve, defined as the limit, is ⅓.

Thus the Fundamental Theorem of the Calculus brings together the answers to the three questions we asked about curves and the areas which lie under them. *How steep?* has the same answer as *How fast?*, and the answer to *How big?* is the inverse of the other two. It was because they perceived this underlying unity that Newton and Leibnitz, who were by no means the first to use the methods of the calculus, are credited with its invention.

10

A Most Ingenious Paradox

Segments of lines have length. Surfaces have area. Solids have volume. The measure assigned to a figure—length, area or volume, as the case may be—is unaffected by rigid motion of the figure. The whole is greater than any part, and is the sum of all the parts together.

These statements are so ancient and at the same time so commonplace that we cannot conceive of their being controverted. Yet in the theory of point sets, a branch of mathematics in which the paradoxes are almost as numerous as the points (and the points are very numerous indeed), we are forced to the conclusion that under certain conditions, involving the most familiar figures of geometry, some of the statements we have made are untrue.

To understand the necessity for this conclusion, we must go back to that unfortunate Pythagorean who discovered that there can be no rational number for the point on the measuring stick which coincides with the diagonal of the unit square, and perished at sea for his pains. From this point, quite literally, we are logically committed to the theory of point sets, although the theory itself was not founded until some twenty-five hundred years later. When, toward the end of this chapter, we find ourselves balking at some of the conclusions at which we arrive, we must remember that here at the beginning we easily accept, in fact, insist upon the assumption from which the conclusions will necessarily follow. Who among us would now renounce the idea that for every length there is such a unique measure as $\sqrt{2}$ for the diagonal of the unit square?

The logical consequences of this concept of a number for every point on the line, or the theory of point sets, will be the subject of this chapter. In the course of it we shall find ourselves juggling infinities and distinguishing precisely between those which are non-denumerable and those which are denumerable; transforming by rigid motion whole infinities of points; selecting single points from infinities. Unfortunately, this is not material that can be skimmed. We can only remind the reader that there is no royal road to even the faintest understanding of the theory of point sets, and assure him that if he follows the rocky road of reasoning he may be more than repaid by the satisfaction he gets from a personal contact with pure mathematics.

We must begin by considering what we mean by "a point." When we take a pencil and make with it on paper what we call a point, we have what for all practical purposes is a point. But a point (mathematicians agreed about the time of the Pythagorean) is that which has position but no magnitude. Since any representation of a point must have magnitude, it cannot be a point. More recently, since the time of Descartes, mathematicians have based their definition of a point on its representation by numerical co-ordinates. A point on the line is a real number. A point in the plane they define as an ordered pair of real numbers; a point in space, as an ordered triple of real numbers; and so on. It is from this definition of a point as a number, and a number as a point, that the great paradoxes of point-set theory develop.

When we start to think of points as numbers, we gain an advantage in handling them. Each one becomes an individual, easily distinguishable from all the others. We can divide an infinity of points into mutually exclusive sets and have no trouble at all in determining whether a given point belongs in a set. All the points on the line, for instance, can be divided into those which represent a real number less than 0 and those which represent a real number greater than 0; while a third set, the single point 0, serves as the boundary between the other two sets.

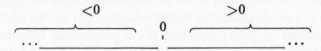

We can make a similar division of the points on the plane by including in one set all those the x-coordinate of which is less than 0 and in the other, greater than 0. Here the boundary set will contain not just one point but all those points with $x = 0$, or the y-axis itself.

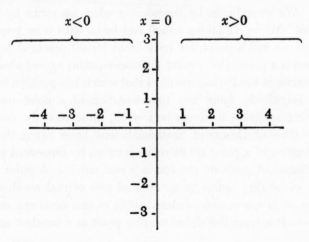

If we inscribe a figure on the plane—let us say a circle of radius 1 about the origin—we can distinguish the points which are on its circumference from all the other points in the plane. Physically, this is impossible; for our drawing, no matter how finely done, must add magnitude to the position of the points. Mentally though, such a selection is perfectly possible.

The equation for the given circle is

$$x^2 + y^2 = 1$$

since, by the Pythagorean theorem, the sum of the squares of the x and y coordinates at any point on the circumference will give us the square of the hypotenuse, which is also the square of the radius of the circle, in this case 1. There are various sets of points which we can represent by means of this knowledge. The equation itself is the equivalent of the statement "all the points x,y for which the equation holds." If we take at random two points, say $(4,3)$ and $(\frac{1}{4},\frac{1}{2})$, we find that

$$4^2 + 3^2 > 1$$
$$\left(\frac{1}{4}\right)^2 + \left(\frac{1}{2}\right)^2 < 1$$

where the symbols $>,<$ are read as "is greater than" and "is less than," respectively. It is clear that $(4,3)$ and $(\frac{1}{4},\frac{1}{2})$ are not among the points on the circumference of our circle. If, in fact, we locate them on the plane pictured on page 144, we can actually see that $(4,3)$ would fall outside a circle of radius 1 about the origin while $(\frac{1}{4},\frac{1}{2})$ would fall inside. Thus with the equation for the circle already given and various related equalities, we are able to divide the points on the plane into various sets. Certain pairs of these sets, when combined, will include all of the points in the plane and yet will have no points in common: A and F, B and E, C and D. These are called complementary sets.

A. $x^2 + y^2 = 1$ the set of points on the circumference

B. $x^2 + y^2 < 1$ the set of points interior to the circle

C. $x^2 + y^2 > 1$ the set of points exterior to the circle

D. $x^2 + y^2 \leqq 1$ the set of points on the circumference and the interior of the circle

E. $x^2 + y^2 \geqq 1$ the set of points on the circumference and the exterior of the circle

F. $x^2 + y^2 \neq 1$ the set of all points not on the circumference

When we divide the entire plane into such parts, even though we cannot physically represent some of them, like the points on the circumference or the interior of the circle without the circumference, we are still dealing with the concept of the whole and its parts in the traditional manner. The plane is the sum of its sub-sets *A, B* and *C;* each occupies a "different" portion of the plane. Yet with point sets it is possible to divide the plane into various pairs of complementary sets in such a way that each set of the pair by itself is everywhere dense upon the plane. Such a pair would be the set of all points in the plane which have rational co-ordinates; and its complement, the set of all points which have at least one irrational coordinate. Together, they include all the points in the plane, which are everywhere dense. Yet, when we remove either set of points, the points remaining are still everywhere dense in the plane. This curious situation arises from the fact that the rational numbers are everywhere dense (i.e., between any two rational numbers there is always another rational number) and that the same characteristic is exhibited by the irrational numbers.

There is yet another unconventional way in which we can divide the whole point set into parts, or sub-sets of points, a way which is not available to us when we are dealing with geometrical figures in the traditional manner. As we have seen, we can divide a point set into a finite number of complementary sets, or parts; but we can also divide it into an infinity of such parts. The number of points on a line, in a plane or in a space is always the same: a non-denumerable infinity. If we divide any one of these point sets into sub-sets, each of which contains but a single point, we have divided the whole into a non-denumerable infinity of parts. Such a non-denumerable infinity is infinitely more numerous than a denumerable infinity; yet we can also divide a point set which contains a non-denumerable infinity of points into a denumerable infinity of sub-sets. Later we shall see that this is sometimes a rather complicated procedure, but now we shall merely divide the real number line into a denumerable infinity of parts. This is child's play in the theory of point sets. By defining each sub-set as all the real numbers equal to and greater than a given integer n but less than the next largest integer, or $n + 1$, we have solved the problem. The integers, a denumerable infinity themselves, divide the non-denumerable infinity of real numbers, which represent all the points on the line, into a denumerable infinity of sub-sets, each of which of course contains in turn a non-denumerable infinity of points.*

The distinction between non-denumerable and denu-

* The reader is reminded of the proof on page 73 and the following pages that the real numbers between 0 and 1 are a non-denumerable infinity, and of the proof on page 75 that the number of points on any portion of the line is equal to the number of points on the entire length of the line.

merable infinities, as confusing as it may be to us at first, is essential to our gaining even a glimpse of the reasoning which leads to the paradoxes of point-set theory and their implications for the theory of measure. We must, therefore, make sure that we have it clearly in mind before we go any further in this chapter. We recall from Chapter 5 that a denumerable or countable infinity (the "smallest" of all infinities) is one whose members can be placed in one-to-one correspondence with the integers, and thus—in the sense that there is an ordered pairing between its members and the integers—can be counted. Such countable infinities include the integers themselves; such sub-sets as the natural numbers, the even numbers, the primes, and so on; and, what is particularly important to us in point-set theory, the rational numbers. A non-denumerable infinity, as we saw in the same chapter, is more numerous than the integers, cannot be arranged in any way so that its members can be paired with them, and hence cannot be "counted" in the same sense that a denumerable infinity can be counted. Such uncountable or non-denumerable infinities include the points of line, plane and space; the real numbers which include a number for every point on the line, as a pair of real numbers gives us a numerical representation for every point on the plane; a triple, for every point in space; and so on; and, particularly important to us in point-set theory, the irrationals. It is essential that we keep in mind the fact that while the rationals and the irrationals are complementary sub-sets of the real numbers, the rationals are denumerable and the irrationals are non-denumerable.

In brief summary:

1. Each of the geometrical figures, plane and solid, with which we shall deal in the next few pages contains a non-denumerable infinity of points.

2. Each and every one of such a non-denumerable in-

finity of points can be handled as an individual because it can be uniquely defined by ordered real number coordinates.

3. The real numbers, which are the rational numbers plus the irrational numbers, are a non-denumerable infinity.

4. The rational real numbers are a denumerable infinity.

5. The irrational real numbers are a non-denumerable infinity.

We are now prepared to follow the reasoning which will lead us to a fundamental paradox of point-set theory:

The whole is not necessarily greater than one of its proper parts, but on the contrary can be congruent to that part.

The word *congruent* here means equal in that special sense in which we use it in the geometry with which we are all familiar. In point sets we always use it in this sense. As a specific example, we say that the triangles A and B below are congruent if, without lifting the left-hand triangle out of the plane, we can, by rigid motion alone (sliding along the page in this case), superpose it upon the right-hand triangle so that the two occupy exactly the same position and there is a one-to-one correspondence between their points. The triangle C, as can be seen, is a proper part of A; but since A can never, by rigid motion alone, be superposed on C, they are not congruent.

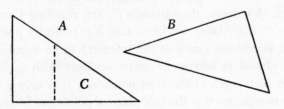

In point-set theory the meaning of the word *congruent* is exactly the same as it is in traditional geometry—superposition and one-to-one correspondence achieved by rigid motion alone. But here the resemblance stops. For in traditional geometry we never find, as we do in point sets, that the whole can be congruent to its proper part. We can never superpose A in the figure above upon C, its proper part; but we can superpose the whole right-hand half of the plane, or the set of all points such that $x>0$, upon a proper part, the set of all points with $x>1$.

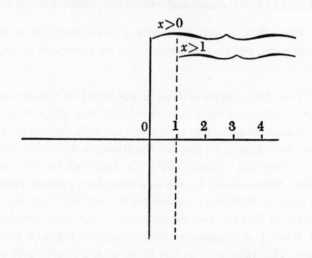

It is "obvious" to us that the entire right-hand half of the plane ($x>0$) is "larger" than that "part" of it ($x>1$) which lies to the right of 1, "larger" in the same way that triangle A is larger than triangle C. Yet, recalling Cantor's theory of the infinite, we know that it is perfectly possible for an infinite set (such as the integers) to be equal (because placed in one-to-one correspondence with it) to a proper part (such as the even numbers). It is only a step to the recognition that the half-plane of points can be superposed on its proper part because the points of each can be placed in one-to-one correspondence merely by sliding the whole onto its part. Since such superposition achieved by rigid motion is the accepted definition of congruence, we can say in this situation that the whole is congruent to its proper part.

In point-set theory this same notion of congruence is found in sets much more complicated than the points of the half-plane. For an example of such a set, we begin by marking off on a circle an angle which is an irrational multiple of one complete rotation of the circle, or 360°. If we were to make our angle a rational multiple (for instance, 90° or one-fourth of a complete rotation), we would find that after we had marked off four angles our next would coincide exactly with one which we had previously marked off. When, however, our angle is irrational, like $1/\sqrt{2}$, no matter how many times we go around the circle we shall never mark off an angle which coincides exactly with one which we have previously marked off.

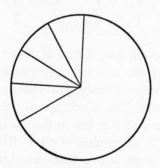

We thus divide the circle into an infinite number of line segments—in this case a denumerable infinity, since each segment can be paired in order with an integer, the first with 1, the second with 2, and so on. The point set which we extract in this way from all the points of the circle consists of a denumerable infinity of line segments, each of which contains a non-denumerable infinity of points. Now this point set can be shown to be congruent to a proper part. By rigid motion—in this case a rotation of the whole point set through the distance of our chosen angle—we bring each segment into the position originally occupied by the next segment in the construction. Since, however, no segment can have been brought into the position originally occupied by the first segment, we have shown that the whole is congruent to its proper part.

The same result could have been achieved by considering as our point set the end points of the segments which lie on the circumference of the circle. Then by rotating the circumference we would place the first point on the second, the second on the third, and so on. A numerical equivalent would be the placing of the positive integers in one-to-one correspondence with the positive integers greater than 1:

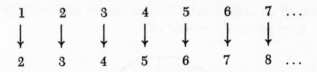

For our next example, instead of extracting a denumerable infinity of points from the circumference, we shall divide the entire circumference into a denumerable infinity of congruent pieces. This is not, by any manner of means, child's play. The difficulty lies in the phrase "a denumerable infinity." It is no problem at all to divide the circumference of any circle into a finite number of congruent pieces. We can, for instance, use the length of the radius to mark off six arcs on the circumference, any one of which can be superposed by the rigid motion of rotation on any one of the others.* Nor is it a problem, as we have already

---

* Even in such a simple problem as this, in point sets we have to decide how to distribute the end points of the arcs, since each shares its end points with the adjacent arcs. (We usually go around the circle counterclockwise and assign to each arc its first end point.)

seen in connection with the real number line, to divide the circumference into a non-denumerable infinity of congruent pieces, since when each piece consists of just one of the non-denumerable infinity of points on the circumference, all of them together are a non-denumerable infinity of congruent pieces. Here, however, the method we used to divide the real number line into a denumerable infinity of pieces, which were integer intervals, will not work, since the real number line is infinite in length while the circumference of the circle is finite. To solve our problem we must resort to a much deeper type of reasoning.

We begin with a circle the circumference of which is one unit in length. The circumference can then be thought of as the portion of the real number line between 0 and 1. Except for the fact that 0 and 1 are the same point, all the other points on the circumference are uniquely identifiable as the real numbers from 0 to 1.

To divide this *non-denumerable* infinity of points on the circumference into a *denumerable* infinity of sub-sets, we first gather together a set (or what we shall call a family, to distinguish it from the other types of sets) which consists of all those points that differ from some point on the circumference by a rational number, or distance. The first family consists of all those points which are a rational distance from the point 0. This family, we can see, will include all the rational points on the circumference since $0 + \frac{1}{2}$ gives us the rational point $\frac{1}{2}$; $0 + \frac{1}{3}$ gives us the rational point $\frac{1}{3}$, and so on. We do not need to bother with selecting points a rational distance from any rational point other than 0, for the points so selected would necessarily be duplicates of those already included in the first family (the sum of rational numbers being always a rational number). We turn our attention to selecting families of points which are a rational distance from each irrational point in turn.

One of these families, for instance, will be all those points a rational distance from the irrational point $1/\sqrt{2}$. Since we are choosing a different family of points for each irrational point and since there is a non-denumerable infinity of such irrational points between 0 and 1, we shall divide the non-denumerable infinity of points on the circumference into a non-denumerable infinity of families, or point sets. How many points in each of these families? Only a denumerable infinity, for there is just one point for each rational distance and the rationals themselves are a denumerable infinity.

From the families, we now gather together a new kind of point set which we can call, to distinguish it from a family, a set of representatives from each family. The first set of such representatives is obtained by choosing from each of the non-denumerable infinity of families a single point, and will thus contain a non-denumerable infinity of points.*

* After all that we have accepted so far, we probably have no difficulty in accepting the idea that we can choose from each of a non-denumerable infinity a single point. Yet this statement—known as the Axiom of Choice—has been one of the most controversial in modern mathematics. It is easy to see that if we have a finite number of sets, no two of which have a common member, we can in a finite number of operations choose a member from each set so that we have a new set which has just one member in common with each of the original sets. If, however, we have an infinite number of sets to choose from, we cannot choose the new set in a finite number of operations unless we have some way of automatically distinguishing the member to be chosen. This difficulty is illustrated in Bertrand Russell's story of the infinitely rich man with infinitely many pairs of shoes and socks. He can easily form a set—either of the right shoes or the left—which has one member in common with each pair of shoes. He would, however, have to choose (in the case of each pair of socks) a sock for his new set. Since he could never complete this task, the set containing one sock from each pair could never be chosen. Mathematicians usually overcome this difficulty with the Axiom of Choice by means of which they simply *assume*, as an axiom, that it is always possible to choose one member from each of an infinite number of sets.

The next set of such representatives is obtained by rotating the entire circle a given rational distance and taking from each family a second point which is that rational distance from the first. To obtain yet another set of representatives we again rotate the circle a different rational distance; we continue in this manner until we have a set of representatives for each of the denumerable infinity of rational distances on the circumference.

It is logically clear (although it may take a moment for one unused to juggling infinities to see that it is) that we will end up with a denumerable infinity of sets of representatives, for there will be one for each rational distance—a denumerable infinity. Each set of representatives, however, will contain a non-denumerable infinity of points, one from each of the non-denumerable infinities of families we first selected.

None of the sets of representatives can have a point in common with any other set because each rotation gave us a choice which, by its nature, could not include any of the points selected by previous rotations. Since the points which we are choosing constitute a denumerable infinity, as does each of the families from which they are being chosen, every point on the circumference will be included in some set of representatives. We have, therefore, by dividing the circumference into mutually exclusive sets including every point, divided the circumference into a denumerable infinity of pieces. These pieces are congruent in the sense of elementary geometry, for all were obtained by the rigid motion of rotation. We have solved the given problem: *to divide the circumference of a circle into a denumerable infinity of congruent pieces.*

The significance of what we have done may not be immediately apparent to the reader whose head is still rocking with non-denumerable and denumerable infinities; but let us consider for a moment the problem of assigning a measure, or a length, to these pieces of the circumference. Among them are included all the points on the circumference. By everyday standards they are the parts of the circumference and the circumference is the whole, so the sum of their lengths should be the length of the circumference. But by everyday standards they are also congruent, or equal. If, in an everyday sense, any measure is assigned to the pieces, the same measure must be assigned to each one of them. There are two possibilities: either a measure of 0 for each piece or a positive measure. The circumference of the circle is one unit, and the pieces into which we have divided it must, if they are to have any length, add up to 1. Yet the sums of the only measures we can possibly assign to them are zero or infinity. We are forced to the necessary conclusion that these pieces—the congruent point sets into which we have divided the entire circumference—*do not have a length.*

The problem which we have just detailed at some length is an example of the type of reasoning, although much less deep, which led to the most famous paradox of point-set theory and an implication in regard to everyday ideas of measure much more startling than the one above. The Banach-Tarski paradox was propounded in 1924 by Stefan Banach (1892-1945) and Alfred Tarski (1901-   ). These two mathematicians proved that it is possible to disassemble a solid unit sphere into a finite number of pieces in such a way that the pieces could be reassembled into two spheres the same size as the original sphere!

Mathematically, the most unusual thing about the Banach-Tarski work was that its paradox of measure rested, not upon an infinity of pieces, as in the case of the problem we have just finished examining, but on a down-to-earth *finite* number of pieces. How many pieces? They did not say. A very large number of pieces? They did not say. Merely a finite number of pieces. That in itself was sufficiently startling.

The exact number of pieces necessary was given, some twenty years later, by R. M. Robinson (1911-   ), and it was very small. Working with only five pieces, Robinson showed it is possible to disassemble a solid unit sphere (point by point, of course) and reassemble it into two spheres the same size as the original. The reasoning which led Robinson to this conclusion was very complex, but basically similar to that which we followed in dividing the circumference of a circle into a denumerable infinity of congruent pieces to which no length could be assigned.

In determining the smallest finite number of pieces into which the solid sphere can be divided for the Banach-Tarski paradox, Robinson began with the simpler problem of determining the number of pieces into which the surface of such a sphere—or a hollow sphere—must be divided so that it could be reassembled into two spheres the same size as the original. He showed how it was possible to divide the point set of the surface into four sub-sets A,B,C and D which exhibit a truly remarkable property. The sub-sets A and B are congruent to each other; and each of them is also congruent to the sum of A and B. In the same way C and D are congruent to each other and each of them, to the sum of C and D. Thus by rotating A into $A + B$ and C into $C + D$, we are able to form S_1, a sphere which is exactly like our original sphere. We then rotate B into $A + B$ and D into $C + D$ to form S_2, a second sphere exactly like S_1 and hence exactly like our original sphere. Thus four pieces were shown to be sufficient for reassembling a hollow sphere into two spheres the same size as the original.

The solution of the problem for the solid sphere was then shown by Robinson to be essentially the same as that for the hollow sphere. Yet there was a difficulty. We can of course extend the four pieces of the surface A,B,C and D into the center of the sphere, but which piece will then include the point which is the center? If we are willing to simply assign the point to one of the four pieces so that it has one more point than the others, then we can reassemble A,B,C and D into two solid spheres exactly like the original except for the fact that one of the new spheres will not have a point at its center. Most of us would be satisfied with this solution, but a mathematician will go to considerable trouble to get a center for that other sphere. Having found a point by a method too devious to record here, Robinson brought it to the center of the sphere by translation * (all the other rigid motions involved in the solution being rotations about the origin which of course could not produce the needed copy of the origin). Five, then, was determined as the necessary and sufficient number of pieces for the Banach-Tarski paradox.

The significance of this paradox for the theory of measure is immediately apparent. When we consider geometric figures as point sets in 3-dimensional space and we do nothing more to them than what we do to the usual run of geometric figures with which we are familiar, we are forced to the conclusion that we cannot assign to them a measure of either area or volume. If the four pieces into which the surface of our sphere was divided had an area, their sum would be both the area of the original sphere and twice the area. If the five pieces of the solid sphere each had a volume, their sum would be both the volume of the sphere and twice the volume. In these particular situations the sum of the parts is not the whole, but twice the whole!

* *Translation* is distinguished from *rotation* in that, under the rigid motion of translation, all the points are moving in the same direction at the same time.

A conclusion like this—completely contrary to every-thing our intuition tells us, to what we have always known with confidence that we knew, and to what we feel is true—separates the mathematical minds from the inherently non-mathematical. For there are always those who want to go back to the beginning, change the rules, forbid such excep-tions, refuse such conclusions. The man who was the founder of point-set theory was not one of these.

Georg Cantor came to the theory of point sets because he was *forced*—this was his own word for it—by logic. He did not invent his theory, arbitrarily, to confound intuition and experience. It is indeed one of the neatest ironies of mathematics that this theory, which seems as completely removed from the practical world as do the dreamy specu-lations of Laputan philosophers, grew out of the work of Jean Baptiste Joseph Fourier (1768-1830), a physicist who expressed his opinion frequently and positively that mathe-matics justified itself only by the help it gave to the solu-tion of physical problems. (Fourier's own considerable contributions to mathematics were in the theory of func-tions, and resulted from his researches in the conduction of heat.) Although the line from Fourier to Cantor is a direct one, it is not the whole line. The theory of point sets is more truly a modern step on a logical path to which mathematics committed itself when it accepted the idea that there is a measure for every length—a real number, rational or irra-tional, for every point on the number line.

Georg Cantor followed this path where it logically led and drew the necessary conclusions although they were con-trary to his own intuition, training and desire and made him the object of an attack which had been unequalled, in math-ematics, since the Pythagorean who discovered the irration-ality of $\sqrt{2}$ perished, mysteriously, at sea.

11

Of Truth Tables and Truth

Mathematics takes everyday words which everybody uses and attaches sometimes quite different and always much more precise meanings to them.

In this chapter we are going to observe what happens to such words—and why it happens—in a subject called the sentential, or propositional, calculus. The sentential calculus, in spite of its formidable name, has a vocabulary which consists in its entirety of the small words *and, or, not, if, then, only,* and the one relatively big word *sentence.* It is a fragment—and we must admit the most elementary fragment—of a great and modern mathematical study—symbolic logic—which subjects logic to the symbols and procedures of mathematics.

The basic logical concepts of the sentential calculus are things which every mathematically minded person knows and uses intuitively. They sound, therefore, too obvious to bother with. But as mathematical sentences (or propositions) become longer and more complicated, intuition is not sufficient to determine with finality their logical truth or falsity. Then a method is needed which is completely formal, and this method is furnished to mathematics by the sentential calculus under the slightly sinister title of *truth tables*.

We shall, in the course of our exploration of the sentential calculus, use the method of truth tables to test the logical truth of certain statements; but before we can do so we must examine in some detail the meaning of its vocabulary and familiarize ourselves with the five symbols with which it conducts its business. The reader is strongly urged to do the simple problems as they occur, covering the answers with his hand and testing his memory of what has been explained, translating language into logical symbolism and logical symbolism back into language, and taking pencil in hand and determining for himself the truth of given sentences. It is guaranteed that he will be pleasantly surprised at the enjoyment he will get out of actually using truth tables.

The vocabulary of the sentential calculus is, as we have said, limited to very simple and common words. These words are used, however, in a precise way which, in every case, seems different either to a large or small degree from the way in which we ordinarily use them. Because we use the words of the sentential calculus all the time, we have a tendency to feel that, like Humpty Dumpty, we have as much right as anybody to say what they mean. We are inclined to object to the meanings which the logicians assign to them. (Even logicians have this same feeling about the words and argue quite a bit among themselves.) But if we are to understand, we must make a definite effort to erase from our minds our own personal meanings of the words which compose the vocabulary. We must consider these words as technical terms to which the logician, like any scientist, assigns the unambiguous definitions which are necessary for the functioning of his science.

The most straightforward way of getting rid of the ordinary meanings of the words is to eliminate the words themselves from our preliminary discussion. So let us begin by giving our attention to the five symbols of the sentential calculus, each of which represents a logical concept.

$$\sim \quad \wedge \quad \vee \quad \rightarrow \quad \leftrightarrow$$

$\sim$ (*Negation*). This symbol, when placed before a sentence, or a letter which we take to represent a sentence, denies whatever follows it. If we represent a sentence by a variable p, then $\sim p$ stands for "not p." If the sentence p is "Snow is black," then $\sim p$ is "Snow is not black." We can *call* this logical concept "not."

$\wedge$ (*Conjunction*). This second symbol indicates the joining together of the expressions on either side of it. If these expressions are variables p and q, then $p \wedge q$ indicates "p and q." If p is used as above and q in place of another sentence, such as "All men are mortal," then $p \wedge q$ is the sentence—what we call grammatically a compound sentence—"Snow is black, and all men are mortal." We can call this logical concept "and."

$\vee$ (*Disjunction*). The third symbol represents a joining which nevertheless leaves the joined expressions somewhat separated. This is sometimes called an alternation. If $\vee$ is used to join our two variables p and q, the resulting expression $p \vee q$ is the equivalent of "p or q." In the case of the meanings we have been assigning to the variables, the expression can be translated as "Snow is black, or all men are mortal." This is called the logical concept "or."

$\rightarrow$ (*Implication*). With this fourth symbol we have what is grammatically called a conditional sentence. The expression $p \rightarrow q$ is read "If p, then q," or, "If snow is black, then all men are mortal." This logical concept is called "if, then."

⟷ (*Equivalence*). The relationship represented by our fifth and last symbol is biconditional. The expression $p \longleftrightarrow q$ is read "*p* if, and only if, *q*." "Snow is black if, and only if, all men are mortal." Here we have what is known in mathematics as "a necessary and sufficient condition" and we can call the logical concept "if, and only if."

As we read over these definitions and the examples given for the relation between *p* and *q* as expressed by each of the symbols, we are naturally troubled by the fact that they do not seem, according to our understanding of the word, very *logical*. Snow is not black and what does all men being mortal have to do with snow, anyway? Surely the sentential calculus does not concern itself with such inanities!

Let us consider these objections in order.

First: the appropriateness of the examples. In the sentential calculus, *p* and *q*, or whatever other variables we use, stand for mathematical propositions. These propositions may be true (*All men are mortal.*), or they may be false (*Snow is black.*). We are not concerned with their truth or falsity except as it affects the soundness (or logical truth) of the reasoning which follows from them. This important fact is emphasized when the propositions are selected outside the subject matter of mathematics.

Let us take, as an example, one of the simplest and most obvious of the laws of the sentential calculus—the Law of Identity.

$$p \rightarrow p \quad \text{or} \quad \text{If } p, \text{ then } p.$$

If we substitute for the variable *p*, the "false" statement "Snow is black," we then get the *logically true* statement: "If snow is black, then snow is black." This is just as sound reasoning as that represented by "If all men are mortal, then all men are mortal." A logically false, or unsound, statement is equally false whether p and q are themselves true or false. If, instead of $p \rightarrow p$, we take

$$p \longleftrightarrow \sim p,$$

we find that it is as logically false when p stands for "Snow is black," which is false, as it is when p stands for "All men are mortal," which is true. "Snow is black if, and only if, snow is not black." "All men are mortal if, and only if, all men are not mortal." Both are unsound reasonings.

The first hurdle we must overcome is this: We must understand that the truth or falsity of p and q does not directly determine the truth or falsity of the reasoning which is based upon them. The second hurdle is much more difficult.

We were originally bothered by the statement that snow is black, but we were much more bothered about the fact that a statement about snow and one about mortality were combined. Snow and mortality, we objected, have nothing to do with each other; it isn't logical to combine them in one statement! We shall not at this point bring up the common poetic symbolism of winter and death, but shall content ourselves with the comment that it is quite difficult to determine with finality whether two ideas have or do not have something to do with each other.

A simple example will serve. A says, "B attended the University of X and he is a Communist." Obviously, A considers these two ideas related. In the newspaper he has noted that a couple of people recently revealed as Communists attended the University of X. Some of those crackpot professors, he thinks, must be turning the kids into Commies! He connects the two facts that B is a Communist and attended the University of X—connects them both in his mind and in his sentence. *C*, who is an alumnus of the University of *X*, objects. There is no connection between the two facts. They do not belong in the same sentence. It is not logical to put them together! Who is right?

If such are the difficulties of determining "relationship" in everyday life, how can we hope to make such a concept precise? The logician answers this question and solves this problem by announcing in a firm voice that, for his purposes, it doesn't matter whether two sentences joined by a symbol of the sentential calculus are, or are not, related. A conjunction $p \wedge q$ will be true if p and q are both true. "Snow is white and all men are mortal" is a completely acceptable sentence from the point of view of the logician. Before we object (we who use "and" too and feel that we have as much right as he to express our opinion), let us remember that the logician does not even suggest that we be governed by the same rule when we use "and." He only says that for the purpose of developing a calculus with which he can test the logical soundness of mathematical propositions, he must have an unambiguous rule for joining two sentences with "and." As an alumnus of the University of *X* he would probably argue heatedly with the rest of us about the "logic" of the compound sentence which joins "*B* attended the University of *X*" and "*B* is a Communist." As a logician, examining the proposition, he will say that *A*'s statement is logically sound if it is true that *B* attended the University of *X* and if it is also true that *B* is a Communist.

In the sentential calculus we are concerned with the truth of certain combinations of sentences effected by "not," "and," "or," "if, then," and "if, and only if." We ignore completely any questions of subjective relationship, like *Should these two ideas be put together in the same sentence?* Instead, we concentrate upon the objective relationship. When we put $\sim$ in front of p, the resulting sentence $\sim p$ can be

165

true only if p is false. When we put $\wedge$ between p and q, the resulting sentence $p \wedge q$ can be true only when p and q are both true. Once we accept the idea that p and q do not have to "belong" in the same sentence, we have no objection to these rules.

There are similar arbitrary rules for determining the truth of combinations made with the other symbols. These five symbols, and the logical concepts which they express, are no longer common expressions of everyday discourse, but the technical terms of the sentential calculus:

Not. The sentence $\sim p$ is true only when p is false.

And. The sentence $p \wedge q$ is true only when p and q are both true.

Or. The sentence $p \vee q$ is true if either p or q is true.

If, then. The sentence $p \rightarrow q$ is always true except when q is false and p is true.

If, and only if. The sentence $p \longleftrightarrow q$ is true only when p and q are both true or both false.

These definitions of the conditions under which $\sim p$, $p \wedge q$, $p \vee q$, $p \rightarrow q$, and $p \longleftrightarrow q$ are true certainly ignore our everyday insistence upon a relationship between two sentences which are joined as one. To determine the logical truth of a combination, we do not even have to know what sentences the variables p and q represent. Given that p is true and q is false, we know that

$\sim p$ is false while $\sim q$ is true;
$p \wedge q$ is false, but $p \vee q$ is true;
$p \rightarrow q$ and $p \longleftrightarrow q$ are both false.

To test his understanding of these rules, the reader might like to mark the sentences below "true" or "false" from the point of view of a logician.

p = Snow is white.

q = All men are mortal.

1. Snow is not white.   T   F

    $\sim p$

2. Snow is white and all men are mortal.   T   F

    $p \wedge q$

3. Snow is white or all men are mortal.   T   F

    $p \vee q$

4. If snow is white, then all men are mortal. T   F

    $p \rightarrow q$

5. Snow is white if, and only if, all men are T   F

   mortal.

    $p \longleftrightarrow q$

  $p =$ $2 + 2 = 5$

  $q =$ $2 \times 3 = 4$

6. $2 + 2 \neq 5$ T   F

7. $2 + 2 = 5$ and $2 \times 3 = 4$.   T   F

8. $2 + 2 = 5$ or $2 \times 3 = 4$.   T   F

9. If $2 + 2 = 5$, then $2 \times 3 = 4$.   T   F

10. $2 + 2 = 5$ if, and only if, $2 \times 3 = 4$.   T   F

True Sentences: 2,3,4,5,6,9,10.

Note that in Sentences 1-5, p and q were both true while in 6-10 they were both false.

For every p and q, we have four possible situations: the sentences which p and q represent can be both true, both false, p can be true and q false, or q can be true and p false. As we saw from our examples above, each of these situations may result in a change in the truth or falsity of the combination of p and q effected by a logical symbol. These various possibilities can be stated most simply in the form of a table. In the first column we list by T and F the different possible situations in regard to the truth or falsity of the sentences represented by p and p. The remaining columns are allotted to the different logical relationships, and for each we indicate by *T* or *F* the truth of that particular combination under the situation regarding *p* and *q* as indicated in the first column.

Since the table for the combination effected by ∼, or "not," is much simpler than that for the others, we shall give it separately and first.

p	∼*p*
T	*F*
F	*T*

In the following table for the four other combinations, the *T*'s and *F*'s in the first and fourth rows across give us the correct answers in our test a few pages back.

p	*q*	*p* ∧ *q*	*p* ∨ *q*	*p* → *q*	*p* ⟷ *q*
T	*T*	*T*	*T*	*T*	*T*
T	*F*	*F*	*T*	*F*	*F*
F	*T*	*F*	*T*	*T*	*F*
F	*F*	*F*	*F*	*T*	*T*

It is important for us to note that in each of the columns representing a combination of *p* and *q* by one of our symbols, we have at least one *F*. This means that for at least one of the possible situations regarding the truth or falsity of *p* and *q* their combination into one statement cannot be regarded as a "true" or logically sound statement. When, however, we construct the same type of table for what in the sentential calculus is called the Law of Identity, or *p* → *p*, which we mentioned earlier, we find that regardless of the truth or falsity of *p* the combination *p* → *p* is always true.

p	*p* → *p*
T	*T*
F	*T*

Since $p \rightarrow p$ is always true, we say that it is a true sentence. All such true sentences are laws of the sentential calculus and, as we have seen, this is the Law of Identity. We cannot be blamed if we are not too impressed with the Law of Identity. If p, then p. So p implies p. We are reminded of the word *tautology*. Our Law of Identity is certainly tautological. Webster says, "With needless repetition, as *visible to the eye, audible to the ear*." Logicians say, "A tautology is a true sentence, or law, of the sentential calculus."

The most profound mathematical truths are as tautological as $p \rightarrow p$, but because of their complexity we do not so immediately or intuitively recognize the quality in them. This is where the sentential calculus is indispensable. By means of its so-called truth tables there is a general method for determining whether any statement (no matter how extensive or complicated) is a tautology—in other words, a logically true statement.

The table which we constructed for $p \rightarrow p$ is the simplest possible example of a truth table. As our sentences to be tested increase in the number of their relationships and the number of variables involved, so do their truth tables increase in complexity. Let us take a statement a little more complicated than the Law of Identity and by constructing its truth table determine whether it, too, is a law of the sentential calculus:

$(\sim p \rightarrow p) \rightarrow p$, or "If not p implies p, then p."

The method which we follow to test this statement is the same one which we will follow for more complicated statements. We take the sentence, beginning most simply, combination by combination.

1. Against the possible truth or falsity of p, we test $\sim p$ in column 2.

2. Against the respective possibilities for p and $\sim p$, we test the combination $\sim p \rightarrow p$ in column 3.

3. Against the respective possibilities for $\sim p \rightarrow p$ in column 3 and p in column 1, we test the entire sentence $(\sim p \rightarrow p) \rightarrow p$ in column 4.

p	$\sim p$	$\sim p \rightarrow p$	$(\sim p \rightarrow p) \rightarrow p$
T	F	T	T
F	T	F	T

Since, whether p is true or is false, the statement $(\sim p \rightarrow p) \rightarrow p$ is always true (as we see in column 4), we know that it is a law of the sentential calculus, or a tautology.

Following the same method, the reader can now determine for each of the following sentences whether it is a true sentence in the sentential calculus. (One is and one isn't.)

$$(p \rightarrow q) \longleftrightarrow (q \rightarrow p)$$
$$[(p \rightarrow q) \rightarrow p] \rightarrow p$$

p	q	$p \rightarrow q$	$q \rightarrow p$	$(p \rightarrow q) \longleftrightarrow (q \rightarrow p)$
T	T	T	T	
T	F	F	T	
F	T	T	F	
F	F	T	T	

p	q	$p \rightarrow q$	$(p \rightarrow q) \rightarrow p$	$[p \rightarrow q) \rightarrow p] \rightarrow p$
T	T	T	T	
T	F			
F	T			
F	F			

He can now by the same method construct a truth table for a fairly complicated statement:

If p implies q and q implies r, then p implies r.

When we transcribe this sentence into the symbolism of the sentential calculus, we get the statement below.

$$[(p \rightarrow q) \wedge (q \rightarrow r)] \rightarrow (p \rightarrow r)$$

To construct a truth table for this sentence, we must first list the possibilities in regard to the truth or falsity of the three variables, p, q and r. We then check off against these possibilities the truth or falsity of the logical combinations of the variables in the following somewhat nested order.

$$p \rightarrow q$$
$$q \rightarrow r$$
$$(p \rightarrow q) \wedge (q \rightarrow r)$$
$$p \rightarrow r$$
$$[(p \rightarrow q) \wedge (q \rightarrow r)] \rightarrow (p \rightarrow r)$$

We leave it to the reader to determine whether this is a law of the sentential calculus. (See footnote at the end of the chapter.) *

Since any sentence of the calculus can be tested for truth or falsity by means of truth tables, the sentential calculus is one of the few branches of mathematics which has a general method for solving all *its* problems. This almost unique quality of the sentential calculus is extremely significant when we realize that almost all scientific reasoning is based either directly or indirectly upon its laws. We are then, in the words of Tarski, able to dissect even the most complicated mental processes by "such simple activities as attentive observation of statements previously accepted as true, the perception of structural, purely external connections among these statements, and the execution of mechanical tranformations as prescribed by the rules of inference.

It is obvious that, in view of such a procedure, the possibility of committing mistakes in a proof is reduced to a minimum."

This achievement of the sentential calculus is all the more impressive when we consider the simplicity of the tools with which it works—half a dozen concepts expressed by some of the simplest words in the language.

* The reader should come out with a *T* in every space in the last column. If he substitutes for *p*, "Snow is black"; for *q*, "All men are mortal"; and for *r*, "Columbus discovered America last year"; he will find that the statement is indeed a tautology and therefore a law of the sentential calculus.

12

Mathematics, the Inexhaustible

What do we mean by *a method* of solving an infinite class of problems, and is there always a method? These are questions to which modern mathematicians have devoted considerable thought, and the answers they have at length come to are among the most significant in the history of mathematics.

Curiously, their interest in what they meant by a method developed from the consideration, suggested for the first time in 1931, that for some classes of mathematical problems there might be no method. This is understandable. If someone comes to us and says, "I have a method of doing so and so," we do not stop him with, "See here. Just what do you mean by a method?" Instead we say, "What is it?" It is only when he comes and says, "There is no method of doing so and so," that we stop him with, "Just what do you mean when you say there is no method?"

This is essentially the situation that occurred in mathematics in 1931. In that year Kurt Gödel, at the age of twenty-five, published a paper "On Formally Undecidable

Propositions of *Principia Mathematica* and Other Related Systems." This was one of the great turning points in mathematical thought. Although the paper was concerned primarily with demolishing the idea that the absolute consistency of a mathematical system could be established within that system, implicit in it was the idea that for certain classes of problems (such as those encountered in number theory), there can be no general method of solving all of the problems in the class.

Although Gödel's is as complex a piece of reasoning as mathematics is ever likely to see, it depends upon a variation of an ancient brain teaser with which we are all familiar: the statement of Epimenides, who was a Cretan, that all Cretans are liars. If I make a statement, "I am lying,'" I have involved myself in a contradiction. If my statement is true, then I am not lying and the statement I have made is false. If my statement is false, then I am lying and the statement I have made is true. Such is the crux of the epochal proof that there can be no decision method in the theory of numbers. Gödel constructed *a true statement which asserts its own unprovability*. He then showed that if there were a decision method in the theory of numbers all such true statements could be proved!

This truly monumental result started other mathematicians thinking for the first time upon the subject of methods in general. What did they mean by a method? Working more or less independently here and abroad, several of them formulated definitions of a method. Most definitions were extremely technical (one of the most important depending upon the idea of recursive functions); but there was one among them the mere name of which evokes a refreshingly non-mathematical image. This particular definition of a method was put forth by A. M. Turing (1912-1954) and is called *a Turing machine*.

Since the mechanical way of thinking was almost as natural to Turing as the mathematical, it is not surprising that when he set out to define a method, he thought of it as something which could be performed by a machine. Said Turing: If a machine could be conceived of as solving an arbitrarily chosen problem of an infinite class, then indeed we have a general method for that class of problems. When we say there is no method of solving an infinite class of problems, we mean that it is impossible to conceive of such a machine.

With a method, according to this definition, a machine could be given a set of specific instructions which it would follow for a finite length of time, depending upon the particular problem of the class that it was given; and eventually—perhaps eons from now—it would turn out an answer, the right answer, to that problem. Instructions for the machine would have to be absolutely determined in advance: do some specific thing until some other specific thing happens and then do some specific other thing. The machine could ask no questions, exercise no judgments, make no innovations. Each problem would have to go in, and come out, with every step toward its solution automatically decided by the method alone. Otherwise, no method.

Such a machine as Turing conceived is not even meant to be constructible. Conceptually, it is very like one of the great electronic computing machines which are in existence at the present time. In many ways it is conceived of as being less efficient than they, for its aim is not efficiency but simplicity. In other ways it is (quite literally) infinitely more efficient. It is in the nature of the infinite classes of problems with which we are dealing that, while a computer may be in a sense "close" to a Turing machine, it can never—in spite of all possible improvements in its efficiency —be any "closer." This becomes clear when we consider a specific and infinite class of problems for which a general method has been known since before the time of Euclid. *Is a given number* n *a prime?* Theoretically, we can solve this problem for any n by attempting to divide it by every prime which is smaller than $\sqrt{n}$; if none of these divides it, then n is a prime. Practically though, we find very soon that n is too large for us to test by this method. Although mathematicians have devoted years to testing the primality of certain interesting numbers, life is literally too short to accomplish this, and they must yield to the electronic computing machines. But very soon n is too large for the machines. The largest number which has been tested and found prime is $2^{3217}-1$. By everyday standards $2^{3217}-1$ is quite a large number, being some 968 digits in length; yet among the primes it is a relatively small one. Since there are only a finite number of primes which are smaller than $2^{3217}-1$ but an infinite number of primes which are larger, "almost all" primes are larger than the largest known prime. Obviously, an actual machine, because of the limits of time and storage, can never solve all or even certain specific problems of an infinite class. A Turing machine, being purely conceptual, has no such limits because it is conceived of as having an arbitrarily large amount of time and an arbitrarily large memory or storage—as large as it needs for any given problem in a class. Only for this reason is it unconstructible.

The mathematical point to the Turing machine is not whether there could or could not be such a machine. A Turing machine is simply a set of specifications, not for a machine, but for a method of solving an infinite class of mathematical problems. The limits imposed by the concept of the machine upon a method are as follows:

The machine is allowed an arbitrarily large amount of time in which to solve a problem and an arbitrarily large amount of paper on which to do the work. A roll of tape moves forever through it. This tape consists of a series of positions of rest which can be visualized simply as squares. At any particular instant only one of these squares is being scanned by the machine. How the machine reacts is determinded by (1) the contents of the square and (2) the internal state of the machine. The square contains one of a finite number of symbols and the machine is in one of a finite number of internal states. On the basis of these two factors, in the time interval allowed, the machine can change the contents of the square, change its position by no more than one square and/or change its internal state. It can have no choice, in the usual sense; what it *does* is absolutely determined by the method. Also included is a way of feeding problems to the machine and of recognizing when the machine has finished a problem.

Such is the conceptual blueprint for a Turing machine. If what we call a method for solving an infinite class of problems (like determining whether or not n is prime) can be used within these limitations to solve any arbitrary problem of the class, then we have a method. When we say that there is no method for solving such an infinite class of problems, we mean that the class includes problems which cannot by their nature be solved by such a machine.

By a method we mean a machine.

Perhaps this does not sound like what we usually consider a precise definition; yet when we begin to apply it, we find that it does define what we mean by a method, and very precisely. The method for determining whether or not a given n is prime is a method in this sense; for, as we have seen, determining primality by machine is common practice and limited only by physical considerations of time and storage.

In the last chapter we described the method of truth tables by which it is possible to determine whether any sentence of the sentential calculus is a true sentence and, therefore, a law of the calculus. It is easily seen that this, too, is a general method according to our definition of a method as a machine. We can conceive of a Turing machine which, using the method of truth tables, could solve any of the problems of the sentential calculus no matter how long and complicated the sentences involved might be. Since all of its problems are solvable by such a general method, we call the sentential calculus a *decidable theory*.

The more limited a class of problems (even though the class is infinite), the more likely it is that there exists a general method of solving all the problems in the class. The sentential calculus is the most fundamental and elementary theory of logic and is, as we have seen, a decidable theory. First order predicate calculus, a step above it in complexity and importance, is an *undecidable theory*. The theory of numbers—defined as all those problems which can be expressed in terms of the integers, the basic concepts of logic, and multiplication and addition—is an undecidable theory, as Kurt Gödel showed in 1931. When we take a more limited class of number problems, like those of elementary arithmetic, we find that we have a decidable theory.*

In the last quarter of a century, as a result of the precise defining of method by Turing and others, modern mathematicians have been able to till a field which was undreamed of by their predecessors: the determination of undecidable theories, those classes of mathematical problems for which there can be no general method. Just how undreamed-of this field is can best be illustrated by a famous problem proposed at the turn of the century by David Hilbert. As the leading mathematician of the day, he gave to

* Sometimes, however, when we enlarge our definition, we get a decidable theory. When, as in the case of the problems of elementary algebra, we define our class in the same terms by which we define the problems of number theory except for the fact that we substitute the real numbers for the integers, we find that we have a decidable theory.

his colleagues a list of problems which he felt needed to be solved. One of these was to determine a general method of solution for all indeterminate, or diophantine, equations. These, a sub-class of the problems of number theory, take their name from Diophantus of Alexandria, who had a fondness for them. These are problems in two or more unknowns for which integer solutions are required. A simple example is $x^2 - y^3 = 17$, which is one of an infinite class of problems represented by the equation $x^2 - y^3 = n$, in turn a sub-class of the class of all diophantine problems.

When Hilbert, in 1900, proposed to his colleagues that they attempt to determine a general method for solving all diophantine problems, he—and his colleagues, as well—assumed that such a general method existed. Today—so great have been the recent developments in meta-mathematics *—it is generally considered probable (although such has not yet been proved) that there can be no general method for solving all diophantine problems: that it is an undecidable theory. Even its relatively small sub-class, mentioned above, presents difficulties. It is not known whether there is a general method for solving the class of problems $x^2 - y^3 = n$. Such problems have only a finite number of solutions. This has been proved. For instance, the specific problem $x^2 - y^3 = 17$, already mentioned, has the following solutions when x is positive:

x	3,	4,	5,	9,	23,	282,	375,	378,661
y	-2,	-1,	2,	4,	8,	43,	52,	5,234

These solutions were obtained by a "method" which works in a great many cases, in fact has never failed to work in any case; yet it has never been shown—in the sense of a method such as that which can be performed by a machine —that it will work in all cases.

* The study of the structure of mathematics.

To show that the class of problems $x^2 - y^3 = n$ is decidable, someone must prove that this or some other method is a truly general method which could be used by a machine to solve any arbitrary problem of the class. To show that the class is undecidable, someone must establish that in it there exist problems, $x^2 - y^3 = n$, which by their nature cannot be solved by any general method. It is quite likely that this particular class of problems is decidable and that the known method is truly general. If, however, someone were to prove tomorrow that the class is undecidable, the result would have great significance: for, by establishing the undecidability of a sub-class of diophantine problems, it would at the same time establish the undecidability of the class of all diophantine problems.

In such a way the determination of undecidable theories—sub-classes in themselves of all mathematics—establishes, as well, the fact of overwhelming significance: that mathematics itself is undecidable. The answer to the question

Can there be a general method for solving all mathematical problems?

is *no!*

Perhaps, in a world of unsolved and apparently unsolvable problems, we would have thought that the desirable answer to this question, from any point of view, would be *yes.* But from the point of view of mathematicians a *yes* would have been far less satisfying than a *no* is. Now it is established—with all the certainty of logical proof—that machines can never, even in theory, replace mathematicians. Not only are the problems of mathematics infinite and hence inexhaustible, but mathematics itself is inexhaustible.

Index